Mennonites in Crisis

by Lester Burkholder

Mennonites in Crisis
by Lester Burkholder

Copyright © 2015

COVER: Stonework is the back wall of Lancaster's Revolutionary War Prison exercise yard. Today it is the back wall on which the Fulton Opera House is built. The stone wall is on South Water Street, Lancaster, Pa.

Library of Congress Number: 2015940152
International Standard Book Number: 978-1-60126-452-7

Printed 2015 by
Masthof Press
219 Mill Road
Morgantown, PA 19543-9516

Table of Contents

Preface...v

Acknowledgments ix

CHAPTER 1: Fall of 1782.......................................1

CHAPTER 2: Visiting with Christian Musselman ... 9

CHAPTER 3: Testing of Faith 17

CHAPTER 4: The Following Weekend.................. 23

CHAPTER 5: Turmoil in Weberthal 33

CHAPTER 6: Visitors on September 7, 1782 37

CHAPTER 7: Two Weeks Later 45

CHAPTER 8: Traveling to Lancaster..................... 53

CHAPTER 9: October 15, 1782—Lancaster City ... 61

CHAPTER 10: Next Sunday Morning.................... 75

CHAPTER 11: The Next Tuesday.......................... 83

CHAPTER 12: About Thanksgiving...................... 91

CHAPTER 13: December 1782.............................. 95

    Christmas Day—December 25, 1782 98

CHAPTER 14: February 1, 1783........................ 103

    A Glorious Reunion—Late February 1783 .. 108

CHAPTER 15: Mid Fall 1783 111

Historical Documents 115

    Henry Martin's Petition................................ 116

    Petition Endorsements 118

    Supreme Executive Councils Letter 120

    Christian Weaver's Petition........................... 122

    Christian Zimmerman's Petition................... 124

Epilogue 126

Revolutionary Adventure...................................... 127

A Review 140

Preface

MENNONITES IN CRISIS is a historical novel based on experiences Mennonite families faced during the Revolutionary War. The history of the Revolutionary War portrayed in most history books glides over the experiences of those who refused to take part of the conquest for conscience sake. The Quakers, Shakers, Moravians, Mennonites, Amish, Dunkers, and the Schwenkfelders all refused to contribute to the conquest on the eve of the Revolution. According to the *Peoples History of the American Revolution* about 80,000 people, 1 in every 30 free Americans, claimed membership in one of these groups. As the trials and struggles intensified, only the Amish and the Mennonites held fast to their convictions, with increasing contempt from the masses.

It is unfortunate time has erased many small intricate details of this true happening. Therefore, we have to create the day-to-day details. This opportunity is used to portray how the early Mennonite believers lived, worked and worshipped in their homesteads hewn out of the virgin Pennsylvania forest.

All the people and happenings portrayed in *Mennonites in Crisis* are historically correct, including their positions in life, their properties and historical applications portrayed in this writing. The only exception is Hans, our main character. We changed his name from Henry Rutt to Hans Rutt, to create a distinction, in this account, between Henry Martin and Henry Rutt. Our main character, Henry Rutt, or Hans Root, was an actual resident of the Weaverland Valley. He was born on March 18, 1764, to Jacob & Elizabeth (Buckwalter) Rutt. This places him at a critical age in this time period. Hans Rutt is not on the 1782 Militia Muster roll call, but he is on the 1783 roll call. Later in life he married Henry and Barbara Martin's oldest daughter, Anna. Henry and Anna Rutt settled on the south bank of the Conestoga River, just across the Conestoga River from Anna's parents' farm. They never owned this property but apparently stayed in the Weaverland Valley. Henry and Anna are both buried in the Weaverland Cemetery. Today Conestoga Wood Products owns this farm located on the left just before crossing the Conestoga River when headed north toward Reading on Route 625. This farm was also the author's grandparents, Michael and Emma Burkholder's farm, which created the initial interest in this historical account. My grandmother was one of Henry Martin's direct descendants.

The farm of Creek Henry Martin, where many of the accounts of *Mennonites in Crisis* took place, is across the Conestoga River from the farm just described. Creek Henry Martin's farm is found in a short lane on the left, right after Route 625 crosses the Conestoga River when traveling north.

The historical integrity of this account is well documented. Many official court records and writings record how all these different substantiated happenings fit together. It is a documented fact that the Continental Congress charged and convicted Henry Martin, and several of his neighbors, with helping four escaped prisoners of war. The original court records, stored in the Pennsylvania State Archives building in Harrisburg, Pennsylvania, give solid evidence, which enforced the traditional legends handed down through the generations. They also recorded the other participants' names, the prisoners, and soldiers involved in this colonial account. *New England Magazine* published an article in 1831, explaining how these exciting historical events took place.[1]

The author's goal is to create an awareness of the struggles the Anabaptist Mennonites went through during the Revolutionary War. They were only one generation removed from their Anabaptist roots in Europe, and they still had strong ties to their homeland. Hopefully this account will reinforce an appreciation for our ancestors' trials. They suffered extreme trials for not taking part in the fighting. Today the peace churches have the freedom of not joining the armed services for conscience sake. The newly-formed Continental Congress had little mercy for those who did not support fighting for their cause, and our Mennonite ancestors received the full brunt of their wrath. Christians resisted and were unwilling to support the bloodshed that went with the Revolutionary War.

After researching this account, and other accounts in this troubled era, it is clear the resistance of the Mennonites, the Amish, and the other peace churches was not in vain. It was a contributing reminder to the Continental Congress to place an individual's religious freedom to practice nonresistance in the then forming Constitution of the United Sates government. The laws created in the birth pangs of this great nation called United States of America, are still in place today. We are reaping the blessings that our ancestors sowed. Our ancestors' trials are bearing fruit in the freedom of exemption from the armed forces we have today. May we be thankful for their faithfulness!

---

[1]   J. I. Mombert, D.D., *Authentic History of Lancaster County* (1839), pp. 298-306.

Acknowledgments

- First I want to acknowledge the Almighty God and the shed blood of Jesus Christ, which from all power and knowledge flows.

- My wife Edna Faye for her patience and support.

- Muddy Creek Library for documents, and to both Amos Hoover and Jonathan Martin for patiently answering my many questions.

- John Landis Ruth for deciphering legal terms used in the Revolutionary court system.

May God receive all the glory!

CHAPTER 1

Fall of 1782

H IS EYES GLOWING WITH EXCITEMENT, 18-year-old Hans Root raced along the footpath bordering the Conestoga River. His bare feet skimmed over the grassy bank. With a flying leap he soared over the small stream flowing from the family's springhouse, which then emptied into the Conestoga River. A Conestoga wagon pulled by six immense Conestoga draft horses was approaching the ford in the river about a 100 yards from the pioneer homestead.[2] The ringing bells on the horses alerted Hans of the approaching team. The shouted orders of the teamsters, the clanging of the bells, the creaking wheels, and the danger present in fording the Conestoga River drew Hans like a magnet.

As Hans came to the ford in the river, he gazed with awe. The teamster's Conestoga wagon (*Englische Wagebetter*) gleamed in the evening sun. A bright blue wagon bed with vermilion colored running gear and white cloth cover over the wagon bed made a colorful sight. Six gorgeous horses pulled the Conestoga wagon that spread the whole rig to more than 60 feet long.

"Good day," greeted the teamster as the team came to a halt. He sat high on his wheel horse with the jerk line he used to control the horses in his hands. A black snake whip was coiled on the side of his saddle.

"Good day," Hans returned the greeting, as he looked up to the teamster. "Do you need help fording the Conestoga River?"

"The Conestoga River is high due to the thunderstorm last night," observed the teamster as he surveyed the raging river. "Trying to cross the Conestoga River tonight will be dangerous. It should go down enough till tomorrow. I will camp here for the night."

---

[2]   They bred Conestoga draft horses, now extinct, were bred by crossing a heavy Flemish mare to a lighter-boned stallion, similar to a thoroughbred. This gave the Conestoga horses the stamina to pull heavy loads, mile after mile.

"Our pasture is available for your team," Hans replied. "I will tell Henry you are here. I'm sure he will want to come and visit later this evening."

Hans ambled back through the crimson woods to the pioneer farm. It was a beautiful fall afternoon with a touch of fall in the air. Hans worked for Henry and Barbara Martin, who had a large family of mostly girls. As Hans came to the clearing, he saw Henry and Barbara's 18-year-old daughter, Anna, emerge from the cabin carrying a small crock. Knowing she was looking for help, Hans offered to go to the springhouse for her. "Thank you, Hans. Could you go to the springhouse and get some cream for me?" asked Anna. "Please take Johnny along. He asks so many questions, and gets in our way as we prepare supper."

Hans took the crock with a smile, grabbed six-year-old Johnny's hand, and ambled down to the springhouse. He enjoyed the cool confines of the springhouse. The setting along the Conestoga River under the spreading branches of a large oak tree was a peaceful scene. He also enjoyed the company of his employer's son, and his never-ending questions. As they approached the springhouse, Johnny asked, "Who built this little house?"

As Hans opened the wooden door, which hung on handwrought iron hinges, he replied, "Your grandparents, Hans Heinrich, now called Creek Henry Martin, and his wife Anna built this little springhouse. They settled here after coming across the big ocean from Europe. Nothing was here but big trees when they built the old log house."[3]

Hans strode down the steps to the edge of the water, reached

---

[3]   Hans Heinrich Martin, his wife Anna and four children, immigrated to Pennsylvania aboard the ship *Britannia,* landing at Philadelphia on September 21, 1731. Many original settlers spent the first winter in a hastily constructed three-sided log shelter.

down and lifted the cream crock out of the clear cold water. Then he reached up and got the tin dipper hanging on the wall and dipped some cream out of the larger crock into the smaller crock Anna had given him. Johnny asked, "Why did Grandfather and Grandmother come across the water?"

Taking the dipper, Hans rinsed it and dipped it into the cool water. Hans took a deep drink and offered some to his questioning friend and answered, "The people in Europe did not understand the Mennonites. Because the Mennonites worshipped God like the Bible teaches, they were different, and some people were mean to them. William Penn offered your grandparents land, where they could worship God as the Bible teaches, free from interference from the government. Your grandparents, his brother, David, and other men brought their families here to Weberthal to carve new homes in the wilderness."

As Hans and Johnny came back to the homestead they looked about their wilderness home with new appreciation. "Your

A replica of a three-sided log dwelling pioneer settlers lived in until they built cabins. (Hans Herr House, Lancaster, Pa.)

grandfather and grandmother built the old small log cabin down by the spring. It was their home when they came here from Europe 40 years ago," Hans explained as he pointed to the log cabin, now used for storage. "Later he built the stone home where he lives now."

As they approached the cabin, Johnny's 82-year-old Grandfather, Hans Heinrich Martin, overheard their conversation and motioned the boys over to him. He was sitting under the open breeze-way between the two stone homes while whittling a (*schiens beesem*) broom from a hickory log. "Johnny, when your father and mother married, we built a stone home for him to live in, and built a roof over the area between the two houses."

Johnny and Hans joined pioneer Hans Heinrich in the breeze-way. They sat on the log with hand-hewn steps, which led to the sleeping loft. Alf rose from his accustomed place under the steps and nuzzled Hans for a good scratch on the top of his head.

"How did you decide where to build a cabin when you came here, Grandfather?" asked Johnny.

"First we looked for a cool spring to supply us with water," Hans Heinrich answered. "We also looked for a meadow with pleasant grass to fatten the cattle through the summer and make hay to keep them over winter. A southern exposure with a bank or hill toward the north is a big help in surviving the winter. When we chose this spot, we built the cabin with the doors and windows to the south. This was done for light, and to be able to tell the time of the day."

"What about the Indians?" asked Johnny excitedly. "Were there any Indians here when you came?"

"By the time we came to Weberthal most of the Indians had moved to the west and north of the Blue Mountains. Nevertheless, we still saw some Indians who came back to visit their elders' graves and some Indian beggars. Once I was in Lancaster on business, and

Anna and the children were home alone. Anna was working around the cabin and suddenly a small group of Indians arrived, asking for whiskey. Anna offered them food, but they insisted they wanted whiskey," continued Hans Heinrich. "The Indians became agitated when Anna refused. Finally Anna threatened them by saying she was calling to the barn for the men to come. She knew she was home alone. But it fooled the Indians and they left without any whiskey."

"I am sure you and Anna had to suffer trials and dangers as you stated a new homestead in the wilderness," observed Hans as he arose from his seat on the stair steps, giving Alf a final pat on the head.

As Hans and Johnny entered the cabin, Hans checked the time with new appreciation. He could tell the time by looking at the specially placed marks on the cabin floor, and comparing them with the location of the sun's shadow on the cabin floor. He now realized this did not happen by chance, but by careful consideration how they positioned the house and windows.

CHAPTER 2

Visiting with Christian Musselman

THAT EVENING AFTER SUPPER, the chores done, and as darkness settled in for the night, Henry, Hans and Johnny walked out to where the teamster was camping. He had a cheerful campfire going, with a pot of hazelnut coffee spreading a pleasing aroma. The horses were hobbled nearby munching on the grass. Lightning bugs were flitting about and the bullfrogs from the Conestoga River were creating an interesting orchestra. The peaceful atmosphere was in soothing harmony with the sounds of the rushing waters of the Conestoga in the background. Henry greeted the teamster with a hearty, "Good evening."

"Christian Musselman's my name," was the reply, as he removed the wooden feeding trough from the tongue of the Conestoga wagon and placed it in its storage place on the back of the wagon. "Grab a cup of coffee and visit awhile. I met the young man earlier in the evening."

Hans and Johnny sat on the wagon tongue. Henry sat on an old stump, with a steaming cup in hand. "*Danke*. Are you the Musselman whose team and wagon were forced to haul supplies when they moved some British prisoners of war from Lancaster to New Jersey a few years ago?" questioned Henry. "Are you on the Non-Associaters list,[4] and fined for not being involved with the war against the King?"

---

[4] On June 13, 1777, the Pennsylvania General Assembly at Philadelphia passed an act requiring all white males, 18 years and older to give an assurance of allegiance. This act gave no room for neutrals. Anyone who was not an active patriot was an enemy. Those who held back for religious reasons were treated the same way as a man who shoulders a rifle alongside a British soldier.

On April 1, 1778, the Pennsylvania General Assembly added a crushing supplement stating that anyone who refused to take the Oath of Allegiance was to pay double taxes and lose nearly all the rights of a citizenship. A mass of arrests all over Pennsylvania against those who refused to take the oath brought on by overzealous patriots resulted. On December 5, 1778, the act was amended removing some of the gross injustices, but the double tax remained.

"Unwilling I went along, just like the rest of the Mennonite teamsters, to make sure my horses and wagon came back," remarked Christian as he sipped the coffee. "This war is also the reason I went to the mountains in Caernarvon to get a load of wood to deliver to Lancaster. I needed the money to pay the double tax Mennonites have to pay because we will not give the test oath[5] to the justices. When I delivered the last order for wood to the fuel dealer in Lancaster, he asked me to deliver it right to his customer. I delivered the whole load right to the barracks where the Continental Army is holding the prisoners of war on Duke and Walnut Streets in Lancaster."

"I understand the barracks in Lancaster are housing many British prisoners of war again," Hans remarked, petting a horse that came checking for any stray bits of oats in the feed box.

"That's correct," answered Christian, "and many of them are Hessian soldiers,[6] whom the British have hired. These Hessian soldiers have a German background. When I was forced to haul

---

[5]   Oath of Allegiance: I _____, do swear (or affirm) that we renounce and refuse all allegiance to George the third, King of Great Britain, his heirs and successors, and that we will be faithful and bear true allegiance to the Commonwealth of Pennsylvania as a free and independent state, and that we will not in any time do, or cause to be done, any matter or thing that will be prejudicial or injurious to the freedom and independence therof, as declared by Congress, and also that we will discover and make known to some one justice of peace of the said state, all treasonous conspiracies which we now know or shall know to be formed against this or and of the United States of America. *Conscience in Crisis.* Chapter 6, Page 395.

[6]   The Hessian soldiers were German soldiers hired by the British. They were hired as units. They received wages, but most of their wages were retained by the prince of the German state they were from. When arriving, most of the soldiers thought they came to fight Indians, not the colonists. 30,067 Hessian soldiers fought in the Revolutionary War. 17,313 returned home at the end of the war in 1783. Only 1,200 were killed in action, but 7,700 had died from sickness and accidents. The Continental Congress offered any Hessian soldier, who would defect, 50 acres of land. About 5,000 of them accepted this offer and stayed in North America.

supplies for the march to New Jersey, I found that I could talk with the Hessian prisoners of war. Many of them are not much older than Hans, but I hear that many soldiers in the Continental Army are mere youth also. Young boys, who were not taught it is wrong to fight, feel it is exciting to march to the drums and fife, and not have to work in the fields. They are drawn to the supposed glamor of army life."

"This war places us Mennonites in a bind," Henry remarked. "Some in the community are questioning which government is our Caesar. Officially it is the British government that our fathers agreed to uphold when they settled in the Weaverland Valley just 40 years ago. The British government gave us such a peaceable home in this new land. I feel we have no reason to rebel against it. Now we also have this new Continental Government who wants us to rebel against King George, and to join the local militia. We cannot fight or do anyone harm because of Biblical teaching on nonresistance. It places us in a difficult position dividing us from neighbors who support this unrest."

"Yes, we have those not taught of nonresistance who boldly support this conflict," agreed Christian. "Occasionally when traveling to Ephrata, I stop at Michael Whitman's roadhouse in the square of Ephrata. Michael is a friendly and genial host, but when it comes to this war he lets no stones unturned in his support for the King of England. Yet it also got him in trouble. One afternoon he was out waiting to greet the scheduled stagecoach."

"It would be exciting to watch the stagecoach arrive in a cloud of dust. Just imagine traveling from Philadelphia to Ephrata in one day!" exclaimed Johnny. "Why, I guess it takes a week to travel to Philadelphia in your Conestoga wagon."

"No, I can do it in five days, Johnny," smiled Christian.

"Nevertheless, as Michael Whitman was waiting for the stagecoach, Peter Miller of the Ephrata Cloister came along pushing a wheelbarrow loaded with paper for his printing press. Michael did not approve of Peter's nonresistant convictions, or his project of printing the *Martyrs' Mirror* for the Mennonites. Then Peter opened the Cloister as a hospital for wounded Continental soldiers and was a friend of General George Washington. Peter Miller stood for everything Michael loathed. As Peter strode past, minding his own business, Michael's emotions overcame him and he stepped out into the street and spat in Peter's face. Peter was surprised, stopped, but then turned away and meekly continued his way, bearing the insult peaceably."

"A perfect example of nonresistance when confronted with violence," noted Henry. "I wonder how I would have responded in an instance like that?"

"Still, this incident was not over. Because of his vocal support of the King of England, they arrested Michael Whitman on suspicion of being a traitor," Christian remarked, as he threw another log on the campfire. "He was placed in a Philadelphia jail and at his trial was convicted of treason and sentenced to death by hanging.

"When this news reached Peter Miller, back in Ephrata, his conscience could not leave him rest. Peter Miller had influence in the new Continental Congress as they had used his facilities as a hospital for injured soldiers. Finally he walked the 70 miles to Philadelphia and pleaded for mercy for his neighbor, although they differed drastically in opinions and lifestyle. After General George Washington heard Peter Miller's plea, he said, 'This man must be your best friend for you to walk 70 miles to plead for his life.'

"'No, Michael is not my friend, but my bitterest enemy,' replied Peter, and went on to recall the spitting incident.[7]

"George Washington was moved and said, 'Your plea is honored. I release this man in your care as a free man. Case dismissed.'

"A good example of returning good for evil. Surely Michael's heart must have burned as he and Peter walked back to Ephrata."

As Henry rose to leave, he cast a glance at the Conestoga River and asked, "Will your team need help tomorrow?"

Christian, also scrutinizing the ford in the river in the glowing moonlight answered, "Its flow is dropping. I think the team and I can cross the Conestoga River safely in the morning."

---

[7] This incident, often repeated as an example on nonresistance and accepted as historically accurate has no official documentation of ever taking place. After becoming aware of this, using the theory, if they held a trial there should be a record, I searched the Pennsylvania Archives for this account. Nothing was found in the official record about this incident. However, in July of 1778, there is a record of a Michael Whitman of Ephrata, described as a devout Tory, who fled the country to safety. His property was seized and sold with the funds going to the cause of the revolution. *Pa. Archives Series 6 XII Forfeited Inventory & Sales.* Pages 292 & 297.

CHAPTER 3

Testing of Faith

Town of New Holland

66 "CAPTAIN M'ILWAIN has called for all the male residents between 18 and 53 to muster to arms," announced Henry as the family was eating lunch. "They want to practice marching and bearing arms again before winter sets in." A militia rider had traveled through the countryside that morning spreading the announcement.

"Another fine to pay," sighed Barbara as she went to the fireplace to refill the crock with vegetable stew. "We hardly know what to do. We cannot muster with Captain M'ilwain and learn how to drill and kill. Our convictions do not allow us to affiliate ourselves with those who are learning the arts of the war."

"If they used the money to build roads, we would have no problem with the fines they levy against us for refusing to muster," said Henry. "But the money from the fines go directly into buying arms and supporting the war effort."

"We need a bridge across the Conestoga River," agreed Barbara. "If our taxes would be used to build a bridge, helping all the people, we would gladly pay them."

"The logic of the Continental Congress is either fight, or pay for the war," continued Henry. "As the war continues they need more men and more money to fight the war. They keep raising the fines higher and higher to those who refuse to muster. My conscience troubles me that the money goes directly to support the fighting. If we refuse to pay the fines they will take everything we have and sell it, again with the proceeds going to the war effort. My heart goes out to those Mennonites in Berks County who refused to muster and the authorities came and placed the men in jail."

"We will handle it like all the times before," Barbara said determinedly. "We will place some money on the table in the cabin. When the fine collector comes we will ignore him and he will help himself. If we have an honest collector, he will take the correct amount. Yet most times they take everything we have on the table and anything else of value on which they can get their hands. Nevertheless, we will bear the injustice with patience. Nevertheless, I do yearn for the peace we had before this rebellion started."

The next day Henry walked in the lane from his journey to New Holland to get some salt to cure the hams from the proposed butchering of the hog. All the family gathered around to hear all the news. "The Mennonite community is concerned about the happenings in Northampton County. Here in Lancaster County we are not being forced to make an oath to affirm allegiance to the State of Pennsylvania and renounce the King of Great Britain. Yes, there were some Mennonites placed in the jail in Lancaster for refusing to take test oaths, but soon released."

Henry sat on the mounting stump used to mount the horses. "Here Dad," offered Johnny, as Henry accepted a drink of cool spring water.

"It appears Frederick Limbach, a Northampton Justice of the Peace, is issuing harsh enforcement of the test oath. Anyone who refuses is placed in jail and they sell all his property at a public sale, with the funds going into the war effort. They jailed ten Mennonite men and they sold all their goods. Their families watched as they sold all their belongings: Cattle, horses, farm implements, household goods, beds, and even the cookstove was unbolted from the floor. These destitute families are facing the coming winter without food, bedding, or even the warmth of the iron cookstove."

"How can we help them?" asked Anna. "Is there something we can do?"

"Some neighbors and relatives bought some of their household goods and gave the purchases back to them," continued Henry. "Nevertheless, the sheriff conducting the sale and Justice Frederick Limbach, loaded their wagons with tools and other purchases they got for a bargain at the sale."

CHAPTER 4

The Following Weekend

HANS AND HENRY were scouting the thickets along the banks of the Conestoga River. Under the spreading boughs of a large oak tree they were rewarded with a protesting grunt.

"Here is our winter meat, fat from eating acorns all summer," exclaimed Henry. "Let's chase our hog up to the barn, so we can butcher it the first cold snap." Later in the day Hans was guiding the oxen back to the barn after hauling a load of manure to the fields on a manure sled. As Hans crested the knoll to the farmstead his thoughts were on an evening squirrel hunt to replenish the cooking pot in the cabin. Suddenly he stopped in surprise. Way out in the distance he heard marching music. *Drums and fife playing Yankee Doodle?* he thought to himself. Stepping to a spot where he could see down the road toward New Holland, Hans beheld the local militia marching down the road toward the Conestoga River. As the militia drew closer, the peace and quiet of Weberthal faded before the sound of marching feet, sharply barked orders and the drummer boy playing marching music. Waving flags marred the scenic woodland beauty, a cloud of dust rose high and the sunlight reflected off glistening gun barrels. Drawn by the noise, Henry joined Hans in observing the commotion.

"I wonder how the militia will cross the Conestoga River?" mused Hans.

"Please, not in our pasture," breathed Henry, as the order "Halt!" sprang up to the onlookers standing on the bluff. With another order from the mounted captain, willing hands stepped out from the formation. Soon they removed sections of the split- rail fence from the fence leading into Henry's pasture. Soon they transformed the peaceful pasture bordering the Conestoga River into a scene of activity. Men and boys were setting up tents, building campfires, cleaning guns, and many other activities of militia camp life.

After a long pause Henry said, "Both of us will go down in the pasture, get all the goats and horses, and bring them into the barn. Oh, and do not forget to tie Alf up out back in the orchard. There they will stay until the militia practice is over." This was done with no trouble, as the militia was busy setting up camp. "Now they will not see or hear us as long as the militia is camping in our pasture," said Henry. "It also looks like we will be spending the winter cutting new fence rails. Our fence is disappearing as campfire fuel."

As the evening dusk fell over the banks of the Conestoga River, Henry' pasture was transformed by many campfires casting dancing shadows of light on the tents. Boisterous laughter and riotous jests, along with occasional gunshots floated up over the bluff from the men and boys below to the uneasy listeners above.

Later that evening after they fed the animals and the evening meal was over, Hans sauntered out to the edge of the bluff. Sitting on an old stump, he surveyed the scene below, thinking about the difference of his upbringing and those below. The activity had slowed in the camp, but over at the edge of the camp there was still lots of activity with shouting and jesting. Noticing activity to his side, Hans turned and saw Anna had joined him in watching the scene below. "What do you think about the militia camping in your father's pasture?" asked Hans.

"We do not have much choice in the matter, do we?" answered Anna as she sat on an adjoining stump. "I guess you are aware that if this rebellion continues to next year they will require you to march with the militia in the twice a year practice?"

"You are echoing my thoughts," answered Hans pointing to the camp below. "Do you think they have any idea of the seriousness of practicing to injure, and even kill other people? Do they have any concern about their own eternal destiny? Is there any concern about the eternal destiny of the opposing army? After all, their goal is to kill as many of them as they can!"

"Some deep and thought-provoking questions are being asked," observed Anna. Suddenly there was a flurry of activity and noise in the corner of the camp below, followed by a splash in the Conestoga River. Then a fit of boisterous laughter followed. "Sounds like they threw some poor person in the river. I hope he can swim and has a good campfire to dry out. This war has gone on for six long years. Six years of not knowing which government is ours to honor. Six years of procurement agents coming and taking the fruits of our toil to feed the army. Six years of being pointed out as a Tory, not understanding we are just living out the Christian principle of nonresistance as the Bible teaches."

"I agree completely, but that does not make it any easier when we go to town, or meet someone who is a fervent believer in the cause of the revolution," said Hans. "Look. Someone is wading across the Conestoga. Now I wonder what they would want?"

"Most of those men camping down there would think they are really brave men, but I want you to know that I think the brave men are up here on the bluff: Those who stand up and are living their convictions of the faith are the brave men," said Anna thoughtfully. "I am going into the house. Wishing the Lord's protection over you when meeting our late-night visitor."

Hans watched the intruder closely from the shadow of a large tree. The harvest full moon was shining brightly, as the clouds hurried along pushed by a brisk autumn breeze. The campfires below had burned down to glowing embers, and only a few stragglers were about the militia campground. Slowly coming in the lane, the intruder stopped at the edge of the homestead, and waited till a passing cloud covered the face of the moon. Then the intruder continued stealthily, not noticing Hans standing in the dark shadow of a tree, to the chicken coop. He opened the door and entered it, obviously intent on securing his morning breakfast.

Hans moved from the shadow of the tree and moved over to the stump on the side of the lane, which was usually used to help the ladies mount the horses. Also the passing cloud moved from the face of the moon and the countryside was lit in the gentle glow of the moonlight. When the trespasser emerged from the chicken coop, Hans was fully visible, sitting harmlessly on the stump.

The intruder was shocked and at a loss of what to say. Finally the trespasser remarked accusingly, "You are of the age that they require to muster for the militia. Yet we see you up here at the farm, and not down at the pasture practicing bearing arms. You are needed, to protect the countryside from the British."

Struggling for words and restraining his reactions Hans replied, "As you probably know we are what they often call Mennonist. We try to follow the teachings of Jesus Christ. He taught us that we are to love our enemies. He also taught us that if a person is hungry we are to help them. That is why I hope you will enjoy your eggs for breakfast. Also I am not required to muster to arms till next year."

"But you are Tory, because you will not fight the British," replied the intruder, visibly calming down at Hans' mild replies. "My pastor Rev. John Carmichael,[8] in the Presbyterian Church in Lancaster preaches that God is on our side. He says that man has the right to fight from the yoke of slavery. He says the bee has a stinger, the oxen have horns, deer have feet for flight, and fowl have wings.

---

[8]   From a sermon preached on a Sunday morning on June 4, 1776. Using Luke 22:36, *Then said he unto them, But now, he that hath a purse, let him take it, and likewise his scrip: and he that hath no sword, let him sell his garment, and buy one.*

My pastor says he is certain man is allowed to defend himself from his enemies."

"We are taught that *Thou shalt not kill* is the path of Christian believers," replied Hans.

"Mennonist are misunderstood. We are not Tories. We are simply following Christ's teachings. *But I say unto you, Love your enemies, bless them that curse you, do good to them that hate you, and pray for them which despitefully use you, and persecute you.* We will do this to all men—Continental Congress' Militia, Hessians, or the British. We are striving to live peaceably with all men."

"I will acknowledge that your response to the militia camping in the pasture, and your giving me these eggs reinforces your words. My response would have been completely different if I had been in your shoes," replied the intruder glancing at the scene in the pasture below. "I need to return to the camp. Our conversation and your actions have given me something to think about."

The next morning Captain M'ilwain came riding into the farmstead on a fine horse, followed by a few men on foot. Henry stepped out of the barn to meet him. "We will be needing a hog to feed the militia lunch," announced the Captain loudly to overcome the protesting squeals coming from the hog pen. "Of course we will pay in scripts at the going rate. Since you have not protested for us using your pasture for practice, I will also recommend the procurement agent to reimburse you for your fence which we used for firewood."

The rest of the family came outside to watch Captain Alex M'ilwain ride out the lane, followed by men dragging the carcass of the fat hog. Henry stood looking at a piece of paper in his hand. "When we pay our fines, we are required to pay in good and sound coins," remarked Henry ruefully. "When the militia pays us, they give us a script payable in worthless continental money. Then we are fortunate if we can even get that."

"We made the right decision last spring when we let the drovers take most of our cattle along with the rest of the Mennonite settlement's cattle over the South Mountain to graze for the summer," said Barbara. "We thought they would be out of reach from the Continental Army procurement officers. But here we have the local militia eating our pork we had raised for the winter meat supply. If the cattle would have been here, they would be eating beef instead of pork."

"I see Captain M'ilwain's officer has not been here yet to collect the fine for not mustering last week," observed Henry as he fingered the coins laying on the table. "We will have to keep anything of value out of sight till he comes to collect our fine."

Later that morning Hans and Henry were cleaning out the barn when a rider in uniform and wearing spectacles rode into the farmstead. "My name is Evans. I am the clerk for the militia led by Captain Alex M'ilwain. I am here to collect the fine for not mustering for the militia last week," announced the rider in uniform briskly.

Henry studied the uniformed rider and informed Evans, "Captain M'ilwain's militia camped in my pasture. They used my fences for firewood, and butchered my hog—my winter supply of meat—to feed the militia. After the militia left we had the chore of cleaning up the ashes from the campfires and picking up all the trash left behind, so our animals could use the pasture next spring. Captain M'ilwain gave me this script and told me I would be reimbursed for the fence and hog."

"I am here to collect the fine for not mustering, not to pay funds," retorted Evans disdainfully as he dismounted his horse and headed for the house. Moments later he returned after gathering the funds laying on the table, and the apple pie cooling on the window sill.

"You will have to present your script to the Continental Congress in Philadelphia," came Evans' parting remark, as he spurred his horse to leave.

CHAPTER 5

Turmoil in Weberthal

T HE NEXT WEEK Hans was in the woods hunting deer to provide meat for the table in preparation for the upcoming winter. With their winter meat supply procured by the militia it was needful to replenish the larder. Hans carried an ancient old blunderbuss, wishing he had his sleek and accurate Pennsylvania rifle. Agents for the Continental Army had confiscated all the rifles in Weaverland Valley for the war effort three years earlier. Hans' precious rifle was one of them. He had worked and saved diligently to purchase the Pennsylvania rifle, and then it was taken. The Continental Congress' procurement patrols had overlooked the old blunderbuss, brought over from the old land. It had been sitting in a dusty corner in the barn for decades. About mid-afternoon he heard the horn used to summon them for dinner being blown, a signal to come immediately. Hans knew it was from his home because most of their neighbors used bells to summon people to the house. The Mennonites felt bells were too worldly, and refrained from using them, but continued using horns for signaling. Hans hustled to the homestead and was surprised to find Continental soldiers, in full uniform, sitting on their horses waiting to talk to Henry. The rest of the family huddled in suspense from their unexpected visitors. Anna was still blowing the five-foot long tin horn, to summon Henry to the farmstead.

Finally Henry appeared out of the woods and approached the group. After the greetings the soldiers explained their visit. "We are looking for four British prisoners of war who escaped from the stockade in Lancaster. Their names are James Bart, Walter Mills, Ebenezer Archibald, and Andrew Lee. Have you seen them?" stated the captain briskly.

Henry hesitated, then spoke calmly and firmly, "No, we have not seen them."

"The escaped prisoners are British soldiers, and they are probably dressed as local countrymen. The enemy has captured New York City and the British army is holding it, which is why they want to go there," continued the captain. After some more questions the soldiers left to question some neighbors in search of their quarry.

CHAPTER 6

Visitors on September 7, 1782

Lancaster Courthouse

HANS AND HENRY were busy feeding the animals and milking the cow. It was still dark with the sun casting a dim morning glow in the eastern sky. Suddenly Alf gave the warning bark of visitors coming. Hans wondered who would arrive this early in the morning. Moments later a whistle drifted up the bluff from the Conestoga River below. Henry picked up the lantern and stepped to the edge of the bluff overlooking the Conestoga River. He gave a return whistle, holding the lantern high. Henry turned to Hans and said in a quiet voice, "Barbara and I, along with some of our neighbors, have chosen to follow the path our parents have chosen. When they came to this land of religious freedom, commitments were made. The British government made promises to my parents. They upheld their promises. They have honored their promises that we will have the freedom to worship and live our lives as the Bible teaches. Likewise, my parents made commitments to be honorable subjects to King George II. My father has been living subject to the British crown for 51 years and is well satisfied of how the Crown treats us. This new Continental government wants us to fight those who gave us and upheld those promises. The local militia consists of mostly rabble-rousers and tavern sitters. We feel until this awful conflict's outcome is decided, we are bound by the commitment our parents made. Also, I cannot reject anyone in need, British or American. The Bible teaches us if anyone has a need, it is our Christian duty to help them." Another whistle drifted up from the river and soon five men scrambled up the rocky cliff from the Conestoga River below.

Henry greeted the first one. "Good morning friend. How many are with you this time?"

"Four," was the reply. "I suppose we will follow the same routine as before."

The five men headed for the barn and disappeared inside.

"Hans," said Henry gravely, "you deserve an explanation. Those men are escaped prisoners of war. Some of them are Hessian soldiers, fellow German people whom the British hired to fight against the revolution. The Continental Army captured them and they were held prisoners in Lancaster. They escaped from the barracks in Lancaster and are traveling by night to New York City, which the British hold. My faith in God and His Holy word teach us that we shall help all men who are in need, regardless of whom they are. I think of the Good Samaritan who helped another countryman, even though they had no dealings with each other.

"God's word teaches us to be subject to our leaders. Since this conflict is unresolved, the original government or the British government is our Caesar. We do not know whether the British Crown or the Continental government will be victorious in this revolution. We cannot be subject to two governments with opposing agendas. I want to live in peace with all men, but these are trying times."

Many questions flowed through Hans' mind. It also answered why he had seen evidences of nests in the hay mow in times past. Hans also recalled days when Alf was growling and restless for what appeared no reason.

"I want you to get a crock of milk from the springhouse, cut a good-sized slice of venison jerky from the quarter hanging in the loft, get a dozen or so of apples, and a pail of some water and place it up in the barn," continued Henry. "Just set it on the barn floor and leave. Then we will go about our work today as if nothing happened."

After breakfast, Henry gave Hans his duties for the day. "Take some rye from the shocks and thresh it. The time to plant it in the ground is here." Hans did as he was told, scattering the dry rye stalks on the barn floor. Then he took the flail and beat the rye from the stalk. As he worked, his mind was on the hidden men he knew were in the barn, but there was no evidence of them being there. After he was finished thrashing the rye, he gathered up the straw, which was set aside to make thatch for roofing or used to make baskets. After Hans swept the rye seed and chaff in a pile on the barn floor, then he winnowed the rye by throwing the rye and chaff in the air. The draft created by opening the door in the front of the barn and the open barn door on the other end blew the chaff away. All that was left was clean rye seed ready to be planted.

Throughout the day they heard or saw nothing of the strange visitors. The only indication was Alf's low grumbling as the day wore on. Anna's comment of, "A bear must be in the neighborhood," brought a smile to Hans' lips.

That night the harvest moon began shining brightly. After all the children had gone to the loft to sleep, Henry said to Hans, "Come with me to check the animals."

As Hans lit the lantern, Henry gathered some vegetable stew from the fireplace hearth, which Barbara had set aside. When Hans saw the amount of stew left over from the evening meal, he realized Barbara knew of their visitors. After checking the animals, Henry extinguished the lantern and they walked up to the upper level of the barn. In the dim light they saw the five men waiting for them. As the men ate the warm stew, they introduced themselves.

"James Bart, lately of Lancaster, but traveling to friends in New York City."

"Andrew Lee, from Paxtang, near Harris Ferry."[9]

---

[9] Paxtang was near Harrisburg, Pa. Today it is in the suburbs of Harrisburg.

"Be careful as we did not invite Andrew Lee on our trek to New York," spoke the third visitor. "He is along because we do not want him to inform the militia of our escape from Lancaster. My name is Ebenezer Archibald, also traveling to New York."

"Walter Mills is my name, also traveling to New York. I could use a better pair of shoes. You would not have an old pair to spare?" Hans went and got an old pair which were almost worn out and brought them to Walter Mills. By the light of the full moon shining on Walter's face, Hans realized that Walter was just a young man close to his own age.

"Thank you," said Walter Mills graciously. "I spent the summer working up at Brickerville digging a water ditch to Elizabeth Forge, and that was hard on my shoes."[10]

The fifth man, the leader or conductor[11] of the group spoke. "I suppose our next stop will be Christian Zimmerman's further up the Conestoga. I wish the nights would be longer so we could travel

---

[10] Many Hessian prisoners of war were offered to work at various projects related to the war. Henry Stiegel from Manheim, owned Elizabeth Iron Furnaces near Brickerville and Charming Forge, Pa. The iron ore was cast into canons and cannon balls. The forges were swamped with orders for cannons and cannon balls from the Continental Congress. Henry Stiegel suggested that with more water to power his bellows he could ramp up production. Just north of what is now Brickerville on Route 501 was where Stiegel's Elizabeth Furnace was located. 200 Hessian prisoners of war were sent and worked digging a 1 mile long canal, 7 feet wide and 7 feet deep diverting the water from Segloch Run to Furnace Run. The additional water flow then provided added power to Stiegel's bellows in the forge. The ditch is still visible today in Game Lands # 46. Segloch's Run empties into the Middle Creek at the village of Clay.

[11] Conductors were paid for their work by the British. For each British or Hessian prisoner of war the conductors led to New York they were paid nine guineas. From May 6 to June 9, 1782, nine conductors delivered forty-seven escaped prisoners. Also the British paid each prisoner of war who returned to the front lines one to two guineas. From June 1780 to February of 1781, the British paid 194 former prisoners upon reporting to New York. *Mackenzie Papers. Return of escaped prisoners, with an account of payment to guides.*

longer. We could walk from Lancaster to the Delaware River in three days if we would travel by day, and on the roads. Yet by night and cross country it takes us much longer."

CHAPTER 7

Two Weeks Later

HANS AND HENRY were irrigating the meadow across the Conestoga River from their farmstead. Water flowing in a ditch, came from a dam on Judge Thomas Edward's property to the north. The water flowed through Henry's meadow, continuing across a small wooden canal bridge to Christian Schneder's land to the west. The dam was about a mile upstream where the Conestoga began a long sweeping turn. Meadow hay was valuable in keeping livestock in good condition through the winter, and by irrigating the meadows they increased the yield considerably.[12] As Henry closed a wooden water gate that dammed the flow and caused the water to flood into the meadow he remarked, "After we are finished irrigating, we will let the cattle graze the meadow till winter." Glancing up to the farmstead he remarked, "Looks like we have visitors."

After they arrived, they were surprised to see their visitor was Thomas Edward, the sheriff of Earl Township. With the sheriff was Andrew Lee, the traveler who had spent the night in the barn a few weeks before. "Are you Henry O. Martin, of the Township of Earl?" the sheriff asked.

"I am," Henry answered, not knowing what to expect. The rest of the family gathered around wondering what was happening.

"When Andrew Lee was your guest a couple of weeks ago, he was with the group as a spy. His job was to find out how the British soldiers escaped the barracks in Lancaster and traveled to New York so secretively. Now he is retracing the route they traveled before the Continental Army captured them, on the banks of the Delaware River north of Philadelphia. On this evidence the Supreme Court of the State of Pennsylvania orders you to appear before their

---

[12] The Lancaster Historical Society, Spring Grove, Weaverland and Blue Ball, Settlement and Development, p. 151, M. G. Weaver.

court in the city of Lancaster on the fifteenth day of October in the year of our Lord one thousand seven hundred and eighty-two," read the sheriff from his official paper. "The Earl Township Committee of Observation has filed a complaint against you. General Moses Hazen of the Continental Army is prosecuting you and placing you on trial for aiding and assisting prisoners of war making their escape from their captors. Will you swear that you will attend your trial at Lancaster Courthouse on the fifteenth day of October in the year of our Lord one thousand seven hundred and eighty-two?"

After a moment of stunned silence Henry answered, "I cannot swear an oath before God, but I will affirm that I will, Lord willing, be present at the Lancaster Court on the fifteenth day of October in the year of our Lord one thousand seven hundred and eighty-two."

"That is satisfactory," replied the sheriff, handing the paper to Henry. "Please sign here." With his official duty done he turned and left, leaving a bewildered and crestfallen family watching him ride down the lane.

"A summons to the court of law for doing our Christian duty," reflected Barbara. "When your father immigrated to Weberthal, William Penn promised religious freedom to all. Brotherly love to all human beings is a Christian virtue we are striving to live."

That evening after they had eaten the evening meal, the mood was somber. Henry's 82-year-old father, Hans Heinrich Martin, who lived in the adjoining stone house was also present. "Our new government requires everyone to drill for training in war, and those of us who refuse for conscience sake face stiff fines and taxes. It is no wonder some Mennonites long for relief from the King of Britain," said elderly Hans Heinrich with a sigh. "When I came over from Europe, I had to sign a document stating my loyalty to the British King George II. Now we have this rising against the King, with bloodshed and unrest. Which government are we to obey? The King of England, King George III, which my conscience tells me is right because of the papers I signed, or this new Continental Congress. I remember my father, Christian, who was in jail in Europe for his faith, encouraging us to leave for America. Anna and I sailed to America for freedom of religion in 1731. From the time we settled here on the north bank of the Conestoga River until this uprising started, we could live peaceably and worship our Lord as we saw proper. This new government says we are obligated to drill for war. We are forced to pay fines and pay taxes for the war to shed blood. The Continental procurement agents come and take our grain and fodder for the army. They take our guns and horses in exchange for worthless Continental money. What is our life in this new world coming to? I wonder if we made a mistake in coming here. Were those correct who wrote their friends and relatives in Europe telling the interested parties not to come because of the instability of the government? Because of this, no Mennonite immigrants have come to this new land for almost thirty years."

"That must be Christian Zimmerman," said Henry, as a horse and cart rattled in the lane. "He is the only one in the neighborhood who drives a horse and cart."

"Yes, and he has his wife Barbara[13] along also," Hans observed, as he stood in the open door, and the light from the fire in the fireplace spilled outside the house. "I wonder if he had the same visitors we did?"

---

[13] Henry Martin's wife, Barbara, and Christian W. Zimmerman are brother and sister.

Christian Zimmerman—Born: May 16, 1750; Died: April 6, 1817. He was a large man.

Barbara Martin (Zimmerman)—Born: March 1, 1744; Died: January 1, 1829.

Christian Zimmerman has been positively identified by comparing his handwriting of his account book, preserved at Muddy Creek Library, with his signature on a plea for mercy to the Continental Congress.

After everyone had admired four-month-old Baby Christian Jr., they all were seated around the table, the subject quickly turned to the sheriff's visit through the neighborhood. "So you and Barbara are both charged and have to attend court in Lancaster?" Hans asked Christian.

"Yes," answered Christian. "When those escaped Hessian soldiers were at our place we served them food in our home sitting at the table, just like we would have to any other visitors. In the other homes, the hosts gave them food, but they ate it outside. According to Captain Andrew Lee, this is why they also included my wife in the charges while most of the others, it is just the man."

"Do you know how many others are involved in this?" asked the elder Hans. "This is hard for me to believe. I brought my family to this new country for religious freedom. Now Henry and our neighbors are being arrested for doing what we believe is right in God's eyes."

"I had a pleasant conversation with Andrew Lee," continued Christian. "He seems like a likeable person. We were his last stop in Lancaster County. The Lancaster sheriff headed back to Lancaster, but Andrew Lee was heading to Chester County, retracing the route of the escaped prisoners," answered Christian. "Andrew Lee speaks German, and was raised in the village of Paxtang, near the Susquehanna River. He is a Continental Army officer. Under General Moses Hazen's orders, he was placed in the Lancaster barracks as a spy to see how the prisoners of war were escaping. When the prisoners escaped from the Lancaster barracks, he slipped along uninvited. General Moses Hazen is charging fifteen men and three women from Lancaster County, with helping prisoners of war escape."

"I wonder who the other people are who are charged?" mused Henry. "I know some of our Groffdale brethren are also involved, but I had no idea so many people are helping these prisoners of war."

"Andrew Lee told me those who are being charged," replied Christian. "In Weberthal, you, myself and Barbara, and Christian Weaver[14] further down the Conestoga Creek are charged. In Groffdale, Peter Summey, Mark Groves, and Christian Weaver are charged with the same offence. In toward Lancaster there are more, along with two more women. In addition they will give charges to men and women in Chester and Philadelphia County. In Chester County they are charging Martin Urner[15] who is the pastor in the Coventry Brethren Church along the Coventry Road. In Philadelphia County 70-year-old Susanna Longacre, is also being charged. She served the escaped prisoner a meal in her house, not being aware who they were. Her husband was not home at the time. Andrew Lee said their group got caught on the banks of the Delaware River north of Philadelphia, by the Continental Militia. Now he is going along with the sheriffs in each of the counties, charging all the people who helped the escaped prisoners of war."

---

[14] We are almost certain this was Christian Weaver, 1731/32-1820, married to Magdalena Rutt. They probably lived on the home farm of Heinrich Weaver on the east bank of the Blue Ball run. His wife Magdalena (Rutt) Weaver was an aunt to our main character Henry (Hans) Rutt.

Christian Weaver—Born: December 25, 1731/32; Died: February 13, 1820.

Magdalena Weaver—Born: September 30, 1733; Died: February 16, 1804.

[15] Quote: One day was passed in a tomb, the dimensions which had been enlarged, and the inmates, if there had been any, banished to make room for the living. *Revolutionary Adventure, The New England Magazine 1831.* No other references are made to Church or Pastors in the records of this Revolutionary account. There is the interesting possibility that the escaping prisoners spent the night in the Coventryville Cemetery found just off Route 23 in Chester County.

.

CHAPTER 8

Traveling to Lancaster

Lancaster Powder House

66 **T**HERE MUST BE FIFTY BUILDINGS IN NEW HOLLAND!" exclaimed Hans. Henry, Hans, and some of their neighbors strode through New Holland on their way to Lancaster. Tomorrow was the day Henry Martin and all the other Lancaster County men and women charged with helping the enemy were to appear before the Supreme Court of Pennsylvania. As they walked on Coventry Road, they passed drovers leading flocks of sheep and herds of cattle to Lancaster. Occasionally they also came upon a plodding Conestoga wagon. The dust cloud raised by twenty-four hooves caused the travelers to step up their pace until they were ahead of the Conestoga wagon.

"We could have taken the cart and the oxen for our trip to Lancaster, but that would have been too slow and rough," mused Henry as they ate the dust of the fast-moving stagecoach. "We cannot afford a horse or the stagecoach, and we will just have to walk to Lancaster. I wonder if Christian and Barbara Zimmerman and Baby Christian Jr. were on that stagecoach? I can understand why they took the stagecoach. With Christian's health problems,[16] and with Barbara needing to be at the courthouse tomorrow, they needed to take the stagecoach to Lancaster."

Late in the afternoon the weary group turned on the Philadelphia Road, and met many Conestoga wagons headed to and from Philadelphia. "They say that as many as 150 Conestoga wagons a day travel this road," said Henry as they walked in ankle deep dust. "There is talk of paving this road. It would be the first road in the new world to be paved. Abraham Witmer is also talking about building a toll bridge across the Conestoga River close to his inn."

---

[16] According to Christian Zimmerman's account book, he had numerous expenses for medicine.

As Hans and Henry's brisk pace overtook yet another Conestoga wagon they were startled by a friendly greeting, "Hello Hans and Henry." Recognizing their old friend Christian Musselman, they slowed their pace to match the plodding pace of the Conestoga wagon.

"What brings you this far from Earl Township?" asked Christian, who was sitting high on the lead horse of his team.

Henry told him the long story leading up to the trial scheduled the next morning in the Courthouse in Lancaster. As Henry was finishing relating the happenings, they came to the ford in the Conestoga River. As the sun was setting with a fiery glow in the west, they surveyed the ford. The swift current and steep muddy banks gave a clue to a difficult crossing. Hans was surprised at the width of the river. This was the same river that ambled past his home back in Earl Township, but now was much broader. Nevertheless, Abraham Witmer's inn with hot food and a cool drink beckoned the weary travelers on the western shore of the Conestoga River.

"Why don't you ride along on the wagon? That way you will not get all wet fording the river, and in case I get into trouble you can get out and help push," suggested Christian. Accepting the offer, Hans sat on the lazy board, and Henry climbed up into the heavily loaded Conestoga wagon. When Christian gave the horses the command to go, they responded eagerly. They knew that their day's work was over once they reached the other side of the Conestoga River. The water splashed as the horses entered the river. Christian gave the horses an opportunity to drink the cool water of the Conestoga. Then with a crack of his whip he told the horses to continue. The wagon pulled easily as it descended the stream bank and into the water. Hans soon saw that he had underestimated the depth of the water, and scrambled to stand up on the lazy board as the water came up over the board. The depth of the water floated some weight of the wagon wheels, and the horses pulled the load easily. Yet when the horses reached the other side, the difficult pull began. The stream bank was slippery, and the grade up out of the river was steep. The horse strained in their harnesses hunkering low as they pulled mightily. When the wagon reached the bank Hans jumped on the ground and helped to push with all his might. Henry jumped from the Conestoga wagon and did the same.

Christian was standing tall in the lead horse's stirrups, scrutinizing his team, shouting encouragements and snapping his blacksnake whip in the air. "Pull Barney! Get up Pete! Easy Solomon! Just a little harder Jack!" All the time his black snake whip was sizzling above the team's ears and when the whip was flicked a resounding crack added to the encouragements. When they finally reached the top of the stream bank, a cloud of steam rose from the heaving horses' nostrils in the cool evening air.

Christian, giving his horses a few minutes to rest and cool down, asked Henry and Hans, "Where do you plan to spend the night? I planned to spend the night here at Abraham Witmer's inn. I usually eat in the inn, but sleep outside under the wagon. If you will help me with the team I will pay your evening meal. Until it gets real cold I usually spread my bed under the wagon. You are welcome to do the same." Hans, being impressed with Christian's whip, inspected it and saw that a small piece of silk had been tied to the end of the whip to make it crack louder.

"Sounds fine with me," accepted Henry, as he helped Christian lay planks down in front of the wagon wheels. Christian commanded the horses to pull the Conestoga wagon on the planks, so the wagon wheels would not be frozen in the mud the next morning. Hans helped unhook the harnesses from the horses. Then the horses were led to the inn's hand-hewn limestone water trough. As the horses were drinking, Hans and Henry helped brush the horses. Hans checked the horses for any sore spots from the rubbing harness. Henry urged the horses to lift their feet so their hoofs could be checked for loose horseshoes and small stones embedded in the hoofs. After the horses had drunk their fill they were led to the inn's corral and fed some oats and hay. As Hans and Henry were taking care of the horses, Christian was placing the wagon jack under the axle, one wheel at a time, which, removed the weight from the wheel. Then he took the grease pot and applied a liberal coat of grease between the axle and wheel. By the time the horses were all taken care of, the wagon wheels greased, and the harnesses checked, the evening dusk had deepened into full darkness. With the horses and wagon taken care of the tired travelers turned to the inn.

"I think you will find Abraham Witmer's experiences interesting," mentioned Christian, as he scraped the mud from his boots on the mud scraper near the front of the inn. "He is a fellow Mennonite who was indicted and jailed for resisting associating with the unrest caused by this war."

As Hans waited for his turn at the scraper, he admired the inn's brightly colored sign of Penn's Coat of Arms that also stated that the inn was established in 1741. Much to Hans' surprise, Christian did not go into the front door of the inn. Instead he went to the side door that entered a large room with cheery fireplaces in use making food for the customers of the inn. Christian explained, "The front room is for stagecoach, carriage, or other customers of high society. Wagoners, drovers, and people who get all dirty and dusty walking, are designated to the kitchen. We common people are allowed to sleep on the kitchen floor, but those using the front rooms sleep in beds upstairs."

In the center of the room was a large board table with benches along both sides. A pleasing aroma filled the room. The cooking food, mingling with the spicy smell from the onions, herbs, a couple of hams and some dried fish hanging from the exposed beams in the ceiling, made the hungry travelers' mouths water.

Christian seated himself at the table and liberally coated some warm whole wheat bread with apple butter. After Henry and Hans were seated, they all had grace together. Then each one took a pewter tin bowl and went to the fireplace and helped themselves to the large iron kettle. It simmered over the fire and contained rabbit and vegetable stew. Christian took three tin cups and filled them with apple cider from a barrel in the corner of the room.

As they were enjoying the food, they were interrupted by Abraham Witmer coming into the kitchen. "Greetings Christian, and who are your two friends?"

After the introductions Abraham continued, "So you are the Henry Martin who helped those escaped British and Hessian soldiers, and your trial is tomorrow." As Abraham, the owner of the inn, sat down at the table, he continued, "I do not want to discourage you. With the feelings most of the upper-class people here in Lancaster have toward the Non-Associaters, I do not see how the judge and jury are going to have much mercy. The judge in Lancaster Court is Thomas McKean. When they wrote the Declaration of Independence in 1776, he was one of the men who signed it. Today he is an avid supporter of the revolution. How much mercy can a person who does not support their cause expect from such a man? It seems the whole country has a mind-set that this war is right, and anyone not out there carrying a rifle is a traitor. They cannot distinguish between an outright Tory, or simply a God-fearing, peace-loving Christian who is opposed to shedding blood. According to the teachings of Jesus Christ we are to love our enemies."

"What can I expect if I am found guilty?" asked Henry. "It is no question that I did help those poor and cold souls who escaped from the prisoner of war barracks. I understood you had a similar problem back in 1777?"

"Early in the war I was asked by Colonel Galbraith to prepare a list of all the able-bodied men between 18 and 53 years old living in Lampeter Township," replied Abraham. "I refused, because I knew he wanted to use this list to enlist a militia. They arrested and jailed me in Lancaster Prison in July of 1777. It was summertime, and my family was close by to bring me food, so it was tolerable. They say the conditions are much worse in the wintertime."[17]

As more travelers began coming into the inn, they changed the topic, but Abraham offered the three weary travelers to spread their bedrolls in the warm kitchen for the night. Still, the prospect of tomorrow's trial was on Henry's mind, and he spent most of the night tossing and turning.

---

[17]   John Landis Ruth, *The Earth Is the Lord's*, p. 329; *Conscience in Crisis*, p. 288.

CHAPTER 9

October 15, 1782
Lancaster City

Square of Lancaster

AS THE RISING SUN cast its reddish glow on the countryside, the group of travelers crested the last hill. Lancaster, Pennsylvania's largest inland city, was the home and workplace of 3,500 people. The pungent aroma of wood and charcoal fires, mixed with horse droppings greeted their noses. Traders used Lancaster as a shipping and supply point for the wilderness west of the Susquehanna River. Shops, inns, livery stables and homes lay in the distant morning haze. Its many gunsmiths helped to supply arms for the Revolutionary War. Nevertheless, the large two-story brick courthouse on the center square was the building that took the travelers' attention. With its white steeple housing a bell and clock facing north and south, it was Lancaster's most imposing building. It was visible from the crest of the hill on the outskirt of the town. It was also where Henry's and other Mennonite brethren and sisters' fate would be decided later in the day.

On the outskirts of the town they came to the Continental Army's Powder House. The powder house was where the Continental Army stored its arms and powder until they shipped it to the front lines. The square brick structure, with slotted gun-ports, enclosed by a brick wall with towers on each corner, was an affront to the nonresistant lifestyle of Henry and his fellow Mennonites. Hans and Henry strode past the imposing structure without a glance at the guarding sentries. Yet it did remind Hans that his beloved Pennsylvania Rifle probably passed through those doors after the Continental government agents "procured" it early in the war. Now it was probably in the hands of some proud Continental soldier, who was using his rifle to commit harm to fellow citizens. It was a sobering thought. His accurate rifle being used to commit murder of fellow human beings. Yes he missed his rifle, but he reminded himself this was a small sacrifice. Many Mennonite gunsmiths forsook their profession and livelihood, rather than making guns to be used to kill fellow men.

One block later Hans and Henry came to "The Barracks,"[18] where Henry's troubles began. The compound, which was home to 800 prisoners of war enclosed almost half a city block. A wooden stockade with guard towers on each corner surrounded the compound. Inside was a large two-story L-shaped brick building that ran the length of Walnut Street. "So this is where our visitors escaped from," remarked Henry as they stopped and gazed at the imposing structure. On the other side of Duke Street was the Government Stables. When the procurement agents scoured the county for horses and mules for the war, this is where they were stabled until they shipped them to the front.

As Hans and Henry came to the center of Lancaster they gazed about in astonishment. The gravel streets had streetlights. Wooden sidewalks let the city dwellers shop and visit and conduct business without getting their shoes muddy. Instead of log cabins, here the residents lived in one and half-story brick or stone homes. Taller homes were either inns or mansions of the wealthier residents. Nevertheless, scattered on the outskirts and throughout Lancaster, were the log huts of its less prosperous residents. The fires used for cooking and heating, and from many forges used for manufacturing, cast a pall of smoke covering the city in the still morning air.

Finally they came to the courthouse in the center of Lancaster. Shops lined the square around the courthouse. Lancaster's two largest inns, the Grape and the White Swan, were both located in the square, and were identified by their colorful signs.

---

[18] On December 25, 1776, George Washington led his army across the Delaware River near Trenton. In a surprise attack on December 26, they defeated the Hessians, German mercenaries hired by the British. Over 900 Hessian soldiers were taken as prisoners of war and marched through the streets of Philadelphia to incite the locals to enlist, and then on to Lancaster, Reading, and York and placed in the barracks.

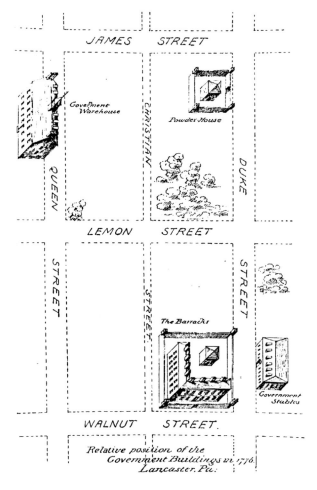

Location of government warehouse, barracks, stables, and powder magazine during the Revolution. The barracks were built during the French and Indian War (1754-1763) by the British to house British soldiers. This was done to reduce the practice of quartering (forcing colonists to house British soldiers in their homes), which was extremely unpopular to the colonists. Late in the Revolutionary War the powder house was moved to the edge of Lancaster on account of the fear that the prisoners living in the barracks would take control of the powder house.

With trembling knees and foreboding anticipation Hans and Henry turned to the imposing courthouse.[19] The square, two-story brick building, was where Henry's fate was to be decided later in the day. Its white steeple housed a clock and bell. The second story had various meeting rooms used by government officials. Off to the side was a single solitary post. Also nearby was a pillory. Around it was a large open area. This was where Lancaster's whipping post was located, reserved as a punishment for transgressors of the law. As they came into the courthouse, they stepped into a large room that could hold 800 standing people. This room served many purposes. It was a justice hall for the local and state government and a place of conferences with various Indian chiefs. It was a public meeting hall for both government business and recreation. At one end of the room was a low wooden railing. On the other side of the railing stood a raised judge's bench beneath the royal coat of arms, carved from wood and brightly painted. Below the bench was a half oval table covered with a green cloth used by the clerk and counsel to record the court proceeding.

As Hans and Henry stood contemplating, watching the busy goings in the hall, the bell on the courthouse began to toll. It signaled the government officials, and those ordered to appear before the court, that proceedings were about to begin. Highly-perfumed men with elaborate wigs, tight knee-length britches and long waistcoats with ruffles on their cuffs, began to emerge from the White Swan and the Grape Inn, and take their places behind the railing. Thomas McKean arrived and settled in his ornate chair. As the presiding judge he had the highest chair and was the center of attention until the

---

[19]   This courthouse burned to the ground on June 11, 1784. It stood on the square in Lancaster. Today a statue stands there with the traffic going around it. J. I. Mombert, D.D., *Authentic History of Lancaster County* (1839), p. 298.

proceeding behind the railing started. The room began to fill with people interested in the proceedings. Most wore simple homespun clothing and went barefooted.

Finally the man in charge of court called, "Brigadier General Moses Hazen of the Continental Army." Out of the crowd emerged a man in full military uniform, responding to the request. With General Moses Hazen sitting in the prosecuting chair the man in charge of the court announced that court was ready to begin. He also announced Mark Martin, whom they charged, was sick and not able to attend. He also announced that Barbara Carpenter,[20] Ann Shirk and Jacob Myers[21] were to be tried separately at a later date, and were to exit immediately. Soon the brisk call came, "Yeoman Henry Martin of the Township of Earl." As Henry Martin came forward, a man opened a gate in the railing and motioned Henry inside the railing.

Looking at General Moses Hazen, Judge Thomas McKean stated, "State the offence!"

General Moses Hazen stepped forward. As the commanding military officer in York, Berks and Lancaster Counties, his presence was commanding. He cleared his breath and spoke with authority, "On September 6, 1782, in the Township of Earl, County of Lancaster, this Henry Martin did unlawfully, basely, seditiously, and treacherously harbored James Bart with meat,

---

[20]   There was a trial for each prisoner of war, with the total trial lasting three days. At the end of each day's trial, a note was added to the end of the trial document. It was written in Latin and translated to: The Court will not have any further discussion on Barbara Carpenter. Was this because of five-month-old Baby Christian Jr.?

[21]   Ann Shirk and Jacob Myers had a trial on October 20th with two charges against them. There were also other escaped prisoners of war involved. Court Documents October 20th, RG File 33, p. 164.

drink, lodging, and clothing. James Bart, being a prisoner of war of the United States, making his escape from the same, to join the armies of King of Great Britain, the open and cruel enemy of the United States."

Then they called Captain Andrew Lee to testify. Hans recognized him as one of the men who had stayed at their farm the night he took food to them. All attention was on Captain Andrew Lee as he identified himself as a Continental Army Captain. He explained how he volunteered for the dangerous job of being placed in the Lancaster Prisoner of War Barracks to solve the mystery of how the captured soldiers escaped. Andrew Lee explained that nothing was seen or heard of the escaped soldiers until they arrived in New York and were reunited with the British armies.

In fascinating silence the audience heard how he joined a group of escapees, uninvited, one dark and rainy night, was forced to travel with them for twelve nights sleeping with various hosts along the way through the day, with Henry Martin being one of them. Finally being captured by the Continental Militia on the banks of the Delaware River, placed in the Philadelphia Prison, identified as a Continental officer, and released. Then returning to Lancaster, and along with the proper authorities, Andrew Lee retraced the route and those involved being prosecuted.[22]

After Andrew Lee's powerful and exciting testimony there was a long moment of silence as the audience savored Andrew Lee's dangerous adventure.

Suddenly, "State the defense," barked Judge Thomas McKean, looking at Henry.

Henry hesitated and said, "As I would have helped anyone in

---

[22] Complete account as described in *Revolutionary Adventure* at end of this book.

need, Tory or Loyalist, I helped the aforementioned James Bart. I helped him as a fellow human being in need, not in any way having intention being injurious to the United States."

After some deliberation the jury declared Henry Martin, "Guilty."

After a moment of deliberation Thomas McKean declared to Henry's bowed head, "I declare you guilty against the peace and dignity of the Commonwealth of Pennsylvania, whereupon it was considered by said justices, that Henry Martin shall pay a fine of fifty pounds, money to the use of General Moses Hazen, the prosecutor, or in case the same is not paid by the twenty-fifth day of March you shall be whipped at the public whipping post of Lancaster County with thirty-nine lashes. In the meantime you are to remain in the custody of the sheriff in the goal (jail) of Lancaster County."

While Hans was watching these proceeding, he was feeling many emotions. *What now? What was going to happen to his employer? How was he going to get back to the farm? Could he run the farm alone?* Hans watched as the sheriff, Thomas Edwards,[23] placed Henry, now a condemned man, into a cage sitting in the corner of the courtroom, until they could transport him to the County Jail.[24]

The same proceedings took place for the remaining thirteen men who were being charged with helping the prisoners of war escape. Joseph Rupp and Peter Groves were found not guilty, but the remaining eleven men were found guilty and all received identical

---

[23] Pennsylvania Archives Clemency File 27 Roll 38.

[24] The Lancaster Jail. Henry and the others were placed in a Lancaster County facility. The barracks where the prisoners of war were held was a Continental government facility and another property. The barracks, recently surrounded with a stockade, was built by the British during the French and Indian War to provide lodging for British soldiers, so they would not need to stay in private homes.

Lancaster Octr 1782

Respublica

1 count
Joseph Rupp, Mark Groves, Christian
Groves, Christian Martin, Mark Martin
Peter Summey, Jacob Groves, Peter Groves
Christian Weaver, Christian Carpenter,
Henry Martin, Jacob Snyder, Abraham
Myers, Ann Shirk & Barbara Carpenter
And in addition to these in 2d Count
Jacob Myers & Martin Myers

1 count, Misdemeanor in harbouring James B
a prisoner of War and Assisting him to make his
escape &c contra formam Statute &c
2d count advising incouraging &c & indeavouring
to persuade James Buck a prisoner of War to
make his escape &c & harbouring & providing
him with meat Drink, Lodging Clothing and
other necessaries for his Aid and comfort, for that
purpose &c — True Bill

Sworn that Mark Martin is so sick that he is unable to attend the Court.
Joseph Rupp, Mark Groves, Christian Groves, Christian Martin, Peter Summey
Jacob Groves, Peter Groves, Christian Weaver, Christian Carpenter, Henry Martin
Jacob Snyder, Abraham Myers, & Martin Myers being severally charged plead Non
cul & do hoc poser &c And the General Similiter & idea &c — process awarded against
Ann Shirk, Barbara Carpenter & Jacob Myers & process exist immediately

And now to wit the 17th Day of October 1782 A Jury being
called came to wit Samuel Patterson, William Porter, John Mays
Michael Straw, William Clingan, Michael Fee, James
Hutchinson, Daniel Ansten, John Rogers, Robert Clark
Patrick Day & Robert Day, who being duly impannelled
returned, the Ed sworn, upon their Oath do say that Joseph Rupp
and Peter Groves are not guilty of the Misdemeanor whereof &c
And that Mark Groves, Christian Groves, Christian Martin, Peter
Summey & Jacob Groves, Christian Carpenter, Henry Martin
Christian Weaver, Jacob Snyder, Abraham Myers & Martin
Myers are Guilty of the Misdemeanor whereof &c
Joseph Rupp & Peter Groves are discharged praying fees

Test & Resp:
James Pinet sw:
Ebenezer Archibald sw:
Noah Lee sw:
        &c Def
John Funk aff:
Henry Lane aff:
John Long — do
Isaac Bine sw:
Isaac Long aff:
John Myers aff:
Barbara qual:
aste Abm Myers
aste Joseph Rupp
Abraham Goodkilly
John Rupp aff as
    to Martin Myers
William Henry Esqr sw
William Smith surgion?
John Kilpatrick sw:
James Thomn sw:
John Kittera sw:

Judgment that Mark Groves, Christian Groves
Christian Martin, Peter Summey, Jacob Groves, Christian Weaver
Christian Carpenter, Henry Martin, Jacob Snyder & Abraham
Myers severally pay a fine of Fifty pounds one half to the State
and the other half to general Moses Hazen the prosecutor & if the
same be not before the twenty fifth day of March next that they
and each of them be then whipped with thirty nine Lashes
between the hours of ten & twelve in the forenoon at the public whipping post & discharge the Costs of prosecution forth com
And Judgment that Martin Myers pay a fine of fifty pounds &
the Costs of prosecution - Iut com
Respublica non vult ulterius prosequi aste Barbara Carpenter

Copy of original court trial.

Lancaster Octo. 1782   451

Respublica

1. Count.

Joseph Rupp, Mark Groves, Christian Groves, Christian Martin, Mark Martin, Jno. Summey, Jacob Groves, Peter Groves, Christian Weaver, Christian Carpenter, Henry Martin, Jacob Snyder, Abraham Myers, Ann Shirk & Barbara Carpenter —

2 count

The same persons also indicted with the addition of

Jacob Myers & Martin Myers

Test.

James Brent, Ebenezer Archibald on Nals. Lee on

4 Def:

John Fink aff? Henry Lane aff?
John Long aff? Benjamin Long aff?
Isaac Bare on. Isaac Long aff?
John Myer aff?
Barbara Myer guilt?
acts Abraham Myer
acts Joseph Rupp
Abraham Grecebild aff?
John Rupp — aff?
acts Martin Myer
William Henry on:
William Smith on Gen?
John Kilpatrick on:
James Skinner — on:
John Kittera . . . on:

Misdemeanor 1st Count in harbouring Ebenezer Archibald a prisoner of War & assisting him to make his escape. contra formam Statuti &c

2d count

Advising, encouraging & endeavouring to persuade Ebenezer Archibald a prisoner of War, to make his escape & harbouring him & providing him with meat, drink, lodging, cloathing & other necessaries for his aid & comfort for that purpose &c

True Bill —

Joseph Rupp, Mark Groves, Christian Groves, Christian Martin, Peter Summey, Jacob Groves, Peter Groves, Christian Weaver, Christian Carpenter, Henry Martin, Jacob Snyder, Abraham Myers & Martin Myers, being charged severally plead non bad & de hoc pose: &c

Process awarded against Ann Shirk, Barbara Carpenter & Jacob Myers & process exit immediately —

And now to wit the 17th Day of October 1782

A Jury being called come to wit Samuel Patterson, William Lowe, John Maize, Michael Straw, William Clingan, Michael Fee, James Hutchinson, Daniel Houston, John Rogers, Robert Black, Patrick Hay & Robert Hay who being duly impannelled, returned tried & sworn upon their Oath do say that Joseph Rupp & Peter Groves are not Guilty of the Misdemeanor &c and that Mark Groves, Christian Groves, Christian Martin Peter Summey, Jacob Groves, Christian Weaver, Christian Carpenter, Henry Martin, Jacob Snyder, Abraham Myers & Martin Myers are severally guilty of the misdemeanor whereof &c —

Judgment that Joseph Rupp & Peter Groves be discharged paying fees, & that Mark Groves, Christian Groves, Christian Martin Peter Summey, Jacob Groves, Christian Weaver, Christian Carpenter, Henry Martin, Jacob Snyder and Abraham Myers severally pay a fine of fifty pounds one half thereof to the use of the State & the other half thereof to Use of Gennale Moses Hazen the prosecutor; and if the same be not paid before the twenty fifth day of March next, that then each of the Delinquents be whipped at the Public whipping Post with thirty nine lashes between the hours of ten & twelve in the forenoon & discharge the Costs of prosecution — Int. comon. And Judgment that Martin Myers pay a fine of fifty pounds & the Costs of prosecution — Int. com?

Respublica non vult ulterius prosequi acts Barbara Carpenter —

Copy of original court trial.

sentences. They all were to pay a fine of fifty pounds, money to the use of General Moses Hazen, the prosecutor, or in case the same is not paid by the twenty-fifth day of March, they shall be whipped at the public whipping post of Lancaster County with thirty-nine lashes. In the meantime they were to remain in the custody of the sheriff in the goal (jail) of Lancaster County.[25]

As Hans watched these dismal proceedings, his thoughts went to the Weberthal Valley. It would be a long cold, lonely winter for many families in the Weberthal and Groffdale Valley.

Hans went over and joined Joseph Rupp and Peter Groves[26] who were standing in the corner as the courthouse emptied. A raucous crowd was forming outside the courthouse. "It sounds like those who support the revolution are celebrating," observed Hans.

"Yes, but when our brethren whom they pronounced guilty leave this room we can be assured their celebration will turn to mockery and jeers," said Joseph Rupp gloomily. "We need to get food and blankets for our brethren, soon to be in the Lancaster Prison. Let us wait till Sheriff Thomas Edwards escorts them out of the courthouse. Then the crowd's attention will be on them. Then we can slip away unnoticed."

The three men watched as the sheriff gave instructions to the eleven men. A guard of armed militia surrounded them, in preparation to march them to the Lancaster County Jail. With Sheriff Thomas Edwards leading the group, they headed out into the street. Immediately the crowd pressed forward with loud jeers.

---

[25] This jail no longer stands. Lancaster Fulton Opera House was built on this location. The rear basement walls of the Lancaster Fulton Opera House are the original walls of the old jail.

[26] Joseph Rupp is listed on the 1775 Earl Township Non-Asssociaters list as a Mennonist. Peter Groves is not listed as a Mennonist.

Cries of "Tory, Loyalist" filled the air. Threats of "Let's cover them with hot tar and feathers!" were shouted. Clots of dirt and horse droppings found their mark. Thomas McKean and the jury stepped on the porch of the White Swan Inn and watched the mob travel down the street.

The sheriff, prisoners and militia guard moved down the street followed by the boisterous crowd. Hans, Joseph, and Peter ventured into the street unnoticed. As they stepped into the street, Barbara Carpenter, holding her son Christian, stepped from the shadows of the cental market, just across the street from the White Swan Inn.

"It feels good to see a familiar face," Barbara remarked with tears streaming down her face. "What do we do now?"

"We need to get food and blankets for our brethren in prison. The prison keeper will not provide the prisoners with food or blankets unless he is paid high prices," informed Joseph Rupp. The group moved to Lancaster's Cental Market,[27] located near the courthouse square, and made their purchases.

By the time the somber group arrived at the Lancaster Jail with their purchases, the boisterous crowd who had followed the sheriff and his prisoners had dispersed.

The prison keeper's wife answered the knock at the prison keeper's door, took their purchases and promised that they would be given to the designated prisoners. When asked if they could see the prisoners she replied, "The prison keeper is busy with all the new prisoners and does not have the time for visitors."

Dusk was falling and they watched a man go along and light the gas streetlights.

---

[27] This market has been in continuous use since 1733, and was frequently used by Mennonites to sell their produce grown on the farm.

"Lodging will be high if we spend the night in Lancaster," suggested Hans. "We can walk to Abraham Witmer's inn on the banks of the Conestoga River outside of Lancaster and spend the night there. There Barbara could get a room and we could sleep on the kitchen floor. Then tomorrow Barbara can catch the stagecoach to Blue Ball."

Old Jail at Lancaster (corner of West King and Prince Streets). Goals (jails) in Colonial times were harsh and cruel. Food and fuel had to be purchased by the prisoner. They had to rely on outside assistance to survive.

CHAPTER 10

Next Sunday Morning

Weaverland Church

I T WAS A BEAUTIFUL COOL AUTUMN MORNING. The leaves were turning into a crimson hue and the geese were honking their song on the Conestoga River. Clear skies promised a beautiful day of warm bright sunshine, while the air had a crisp bite of winter to it.

The whole family, missing one key person, was preparing to attend church services at Weaverland. Hans had put on a clean pair of broadfall pantaloons and a homespun white shirt. He wished he had a pair of suspenders, but only the wealthy could afford this novelty. A small rope had to suffice to keep his pantaloons in place.

As Hans came down the board steps hewn into two logs from his attic sleeping loft he took special note of Anna, as she dressed baby Jacob. Her blue striped dress, and plain white homespun waist gown contrasted nicely with her colored apron. A stiffened sun bonnet completed her attire. Hans had seen Anna taking home-grown flax, and spinning it with a wheel until she had thread. Then taking the thread in a loom, she had woven the threads to make cloth. Finally, dying the completed cloth she then hand sewed it into the clothes she was wearing today. He also saw that the buttons she had asked him to carve out of bone were now colored a pleasing blue. She had sewed them neatly on the front of her waist gown. As Hans considered this, the thought that Anna would make a good wife for some fortunate young man some day came to his mind. Yet with the added responsibility, because of Henry not being present, and the sacredness of the day, his thought was fleeting.

Usually the family walked to church. Barbara, because of her condition, would normally have stayed at home. With Henry in jail she was planning to attend church, but by horseback instead of walking. Hans had saddled their old work horse and led him alongside the mounting stump alongside the house. Barbara came and using the steps hewn into the mounting stump easily climbed up to the level of the saddle on the horse and then sat on it. Anna gave one-year-old baby Jacob, bundled up for the cool morning weather, into Barbara's arms. A blanket was wrapped around Barbara and Jacob, and they were ready to proceed on the two-mile journey to Weaverland Church.

As they traveled, Barbara mused. "I believe this is the first time Henry is missing church services since we built it in 1766. Before Weaverland Church was built, we had services in the homes, sometimes traveling up to ten miles to attend church. Sometimes we had to travel all the way to Groffdale to church, and then it was so full in the person's home. Some people objected to building a church, insisting our homes were good enough to worship in. As the settlement grew, and with the need for a school, it was decided to build a large building with living quarters in it for the caretaker. Now we have a designated place for worship services. We have it so good with a church building so close to home."

As the Martin family turned into the grove of trees where the Weaverland Meetinghouse nestled, they noticed an unusually large gathering of horses and people. Hans led Barbara's horse to one of the many dismounting blocks and Barbara dismounted her stead. Hans then took the horse and tied it to a hitching post under a shady tree. As he tied the horse, Hans thought he recognized Bishop Christian Burkholder's horse, which Christian would have ridden from Groffdale that morning.

Turning to the church building Hans had a new appreciation for the large stone building with a steep wood-shingled roof. He had never considered how fortunate they were being able to gather the whole community together to worship in one building. *At special occasions there must be 250 people worshipping together. We could never have that many people together in our homes,* mused Hans as he stepped through the church door. He found his seat on one of the benches made of two-inch thick oaken planks, about a foot wide, supported by four, stout two-inch oak sticks.

In the middle of the church was a long pine table where the song leaders sat along three sides. They patterned this after when they held the church services in private homes. At that time few songbooks were available and gathering the lead singers around the table of the homes was necessary. Along the north side of the building and facing the end of the singers' table was a bench for the ministers.

One of the song leaders passed out the limited supply of songbooks to those who were interested in learning to sing from songbooks, signaling that the services were to begin. Then a song leader announced a hymn, read the words of the first chapter of the hymn for those who could not read, or had no songbooks, and then started the hymn. After the first chapter was sung the singing came to a halt and the song leader read the second chapter of the song. After the second chapter was read the song leader started the song again. As they were singing, the ministry came in and sat on the minister's bench. *Bishop Christian Burkholder is here from the Groffdale District, and our regular Minister Henry Martin will be conducting the worship services,* mused Hans as the ministry sat. *I wonder how Minister Henry Martin[28] feels about his cousin and namesake being in prison as he preaches?* When the song was finished Henry Martin stood at the end of the singers' table and preached an opening sermon. He closed his opening

---

[28] Minister Henry Martin and the Henry Martin in jail were cousins. Minister Henry Martin was ordained Bishop around 1809. Minister Henry Martin was the son of Pioneer David Martin. David Martin was 91 years old when his nephew was jailed.

remarks with a call to prayer and all the worshipers fell to their knees in a silent prayer. When Minister Henry Martin said amen, the congregation stood and stayed standing in the direction they were kneeling, with their backs to the deacon. The deacon read the Bible text Bishop Christian Burkholder had chosen for the sermon. When the deacon had read the text and was finished, Christian Burkholder stepped to the end of the singers' table and opened his sermon with, "Please be seated." The congregation complied. After Christian had completed his sermon, an opportunity for testimony from fellow ordained ministers was given. Christian then led the kneeling congregation in an audible prayer. When the prayer was over the congregation stood, again facing the direction they had been kneeling, while the minister gave the benediction. The minister then invited the congregation to sit and they sung a hymn before the service closed. All of the service was in the German language.

The services being over, the congregation gathered outside to fellowship together.

After Hans had related the week's happenings to the group of men gathered around him, the question was asked, "Is there anything we can do to help?"

One man suggested that a letter of recommendation vouching for the integrity and lifestyle of Henry Martin and the rest of the neighbors imprisoned might help. This petition could be taken to Philadelphia and read before the Supreme Executive Council, the highest court of law in the new Continental government. All agreed this might help convince the court to release their brothers in the faith.

The schoolmaster was asked if he could write a letter of recommendation in English, the language of the government.

Since the Mennonites spoke German few of the people could write English. The schoolmaster agreed and said he would prepare it and leave room for anybody willing to add their signature to endorse it.

It was also encouraged to go and visit Henry in jail and to take food and clothing along, as the jail keepers only provided a bare minium of provisions.

CHAPTER 11

The Next Tuesday

Old Prison

LONG BEFORE THE SUN WAS UP Hans was awoken sharply by the clatter in the kitchen below. Today the neighborhood was getting together to finish Henry's fall work. As soon as he emerged from his warm cocoon of covers, he shivered. Traces of the late autumn snow, which had fallen sometime during the night, had filtered through the wooden shingle roof onto the loft's wooden floor. As Hans struggled into his clothes, he thought of the work before them. The rest of the corn had to be husked and cribbed. The rye shucks had to be spread on the barn floor and the grain flailed out to be stored in the granary. After Hans came to the center portion of the loft connecting the double house, he descended the log steps. There the dogs greeted him warmly with their wet noses, asking him with their eyes, "Let's go hunt deer today!"

As Hans entered the cabin, Anna was down before the fireplace stirring the hot coals to get the fire going. She was preparing the fire to roast some cut of meat from the deer Hans had shot yesterday. Barbara and Anna had been busy the previous day preparing food. Vegetables must be cooked and food prepared for the large group of people expected today. Barbara was not feeling the best and most of the workload fell to her oldest daughters.

Hans grabbed the two wooden buckets setting in the corner, and headed out the door. Just outside the door he took a wooden neck yoke off the wall, then hooked the two buckets to the rawhide strip attached to the yoke. Placing the yoke around his neck, he headed for the spring. As he reached the bluff overlooking the Conestoga River and the Weberthal Valley, he stopped to marvel. The sun was casting a reddish glow over the freshly fallen snow. The Welsh Mountain in the background highlighted a flock of Canadian geese winging their way south. Looking southeast, pillars of smoke from neighboring cabins reached high into the wind still autumn sky. *Is there anywhere in the world as beautiful as the Weberthal Valley?"* mused Hans. But then he thought of the black cloud they were facing. Henry, and many other Mennonite men were imprisoned in the Lancaster County Jail with an uncertain future, yet having done no wrong in God's eyes. After a moment of meditation Hans continued down the bluff to the spring. After filling the buckets, Hans attached them to the rawhide strips, placed the yoke around his neck and headed for the cabins. Coming back to the cabins, he entered the door and saw elderly Heinrich Martin. "Good morning Heinrich," said Hans as he poured some water into the pot that was in the fireplace.

Heinrich, who was seated at the rough hand-hewn log table reading his Bible replied, "And a beautiful God-given morning we are blessed with. How many people should we expect to show up this morning?"

"I suspect most of the community will come," Hans answered. "The schoolmaster is also coming. He wrote a plea for mercy to present to the Supreme Executive Council. Everyone who can agree with what he wrote is to sign it. Then they will send it to Philadelphia to be read to the Supreme Executive Council of the Commonwealth of Pennsylvania. Hopefully it will touch some hearts, and they will release Henry and the rest of the men from jail."

Later in the day Hans was working with a group of men harvesting the corn crop. They were cutting the dry corn stalk and ears, and hauling it close to the barn where they shocked it. They would husk the corn later and use the stalks for feed or bedding. A neighbor asked Hans, "Have you heard about the outcome of the people arrested for helping the escaped prisoners of war down toward Philadelphia?"

"Yes, we received news that Martin Urner, a minister from the Coventry Church was arrested," Hans answered. "He was found guilty for helping the same men who came through the Weaverland Valley and received the same fines as everyone else involved did. Captain Andrew Lee, the Continental spy at the trial at the Lancaster Courthouse reported one day was spent hiding in a place hollowed out underground for the escapees in a graveyard. I wonder if Coventryville is the place where they hid in the graveyard?"

"Coventry is along the Coventry Road, the main road from here to Philadelphia,"[29] remarked a fellow worker. We go through there whenever we take produce to Philadelphia."

"Were anymore people involved?"

"Susanna Longacre from Chester County was also arrested and sentenced like our brethren," continued Hans. "She is 70 years old, and all she did was give those men a meal, having no idea they were escaped prisoners of war. Her husband tried to appear in her place at the trial. The court ordered the trial held up one day so she could be there and be tried."

"Did Susanna Longacre receive the same sentence as all the men did?" asked another fellow worker. "A fifty-pound fine and thirty-nine lashes at the County whipping post?"

"That is correct," answered Hans. "It appears there was no mercy for being a woman or her age. How is a 70-year-old couple expected to pay a 50-pound fine? Closer to Philadelphia they arrested another man, also receiving the same sentence."

Another helper remarked, "You can follow the path those prisoners of war took by the location of those who helped them and were later arrested. Captain Andrew Lee's memory was good considering they did all their traveling at night."

---

[29] Today Coventry Road is Route 23.

A few days later Minister Henry Martin stopped in. He was heading home from bringing Barbara Carpenter home. "The court ruled that Ann Shirk and Barbara Carpenter were to be released and were free to go home," said Henry Martin over a cup of tea. "The two men whom they tried with them on October 20 were found guilty and were sentenced with the same fines as the other Mennonite men received. I took food and blankets to the Mennonite Brethren in jail. With winter coming on they will need them. The conditions in jail are not good, but at least they can keep each other company."

CHAPTER 12

About Thanksgiving

THE HARVEST MOON was shining brightly on the thin ice forming on the Conestoga River. The Canadian geese honked loudly as they headed south to a warmer climate.

I hear cattle bells, mused Hans as he finished his evening chores in the barn.

As Hans walked to the house Johnny came running. "Mother says the cattle are coming back for the winter!" he exclaimed. "Why were they gone for the summer? Is the grass better north over the south mountain?"

Stooping down and taking his little friend on his knee Hans explained, "No, the cattle were taken over the mountain in the spring, to get further away from the procurement agents of the Continental Armies. This war is mostly a summer activity, and many soldiers go home for the winter, so the drovers bring the community's cattle home for the winter."

The drovers brought Henry's cattle to the barn. After a friendly greeting Hans asked, "Where were you all this summer?"

As the drovers' dogs guided the cattle into the barn, the one weathered and tanned drover answered, "We spent the summer in the foothills of the famous Blue Mountains, near the towns of Jones, Stumptown, and Bethel. The Swatara Creek up there has plenty of water. But the wolves and bears are more plentiful, and you need to keep a fire going all night to keep them away. It will feel good to sleep in a bed at home tonight.[30]

---

[30] *Pennsylvania Archives 1st Series VIII*, pp. 328-329, Document 207. Today Jones is called Jonestown, Stumptown is now named Fredericksburg, and Bethel's name was not changed.

CHAPTER 13

December 1782

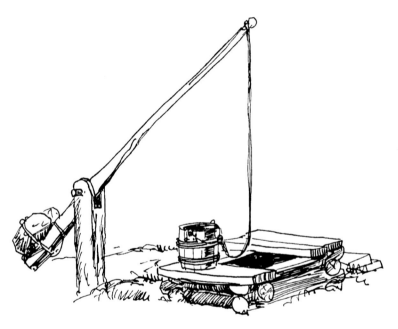

Colonial Well

"A LETTER FROM FATHER!" exclaimed Anna, as she came up the lane. She received it from a neighbor who had just come from taking food and fuel to the men in the Lancaster Jail. The petition the neighbors had signed and sent to the Supreme Executive Council had not brought any changes to the sentence. Excitedly the family gathered around as Barbara unfolded the precious letter.

As she scanned the letter Barbara said, "Henry is doing well. He says life in jail would be almost unbearable, but with many of his fellow Mennonite neighbors in the same position, they can encourage each other. Father also wishes you to have a Happy Birthday Anna. He finds it hard to believe he has an eighteen-year-old daughter! They have released two of the men.[31] Each of those men personally got someone to write their own petition, in English, and then signed their name to the writing. Then they sent the petitions to the Supreme Executive Council in Philadelphia. The Council read and debated each of the Mennonite men's petitions on December the second day of December 1782. The Council decided to reduce the fines by 66%. The men were able to pay the reduced amount, and are now free. Since this worked for these men, the others also wrote petitions and have their hopes high for a favorable outcome. He also writes they have sent an appeal to Peter Miller of the Ephrata Cloister. Peter Miller has connections with the Continental government. They have come to him for printing work and used the Cloister to help feed and nurse injured soldiers back to health. Father wishes the family well and asks that we keep praying for him and the rest of those in Lancaster Prison."

---

[31] Jacob Groves and Christian Groves were the first to be released. *Conscience in Crisis,* p. 506. We have no information on whom they were or where they lived. Both of them were listed as Mennonites in the Earl Township Non-Associaters list. *Conscience in Crisis,* p. 254.

CHRISTMAS DAY—DECEMBER 25, 1782

Hans looked out over the Weaverland Valley from the bluff the Henry Martin homestead was located on and saw a beautiful peaceful winter scene. The cold still air, the snow-covered ground, the pillars of smoke rising straight and tall from the neighbors' chimneys did little to still the turmoil in his heart. More than two months had passed and Henry was still in jail in Lancaster.

Today was Christmas, the day of Christ's birth. It was debated in the Mennonite circles how this event was to be observed. The Catholic Church in the old land celebrated extensively about Jesus Christ's birth. The early Mennonite Church leaders felt they overdid this. They felt since there is no Biblical record of the exact date of Christ's birth large celebrations were not proper. No church services were planned, but out of respect for their non-Mennonite neighbors they did not work outdoors. They planned a day of rest and maybe they could expect some visitors. Barbara also was not feeling well and was not going out in public. Late in the afternoon Hans was out playing in the snow with the younger children. "Let's do it again," pleaded Johnny, after a long slide down the steep snow-covered bluff and across the ice-covered Conestoga River.

As Hans retrieved the homemade sled from the snow bank which had just brought them to a stop in a flurry of flying snow, Hans' breath was a cloud of vapor to rise in the brisk winter air as he exclaimed, "That was fun! But it looks like we are getting company. Look. Those travelers are turning in our lane. It looks like Minister Henry Martin and his wife. I wonder if they have any news from the men in Lancaster Jail?"

A short time later everyone was seated around the kitchen table. Even Hans Heinrich ventured out in the cold winter weather to welcome the visitors. "I have good news, though it is not about our Weaverland brethren in Lancaster," exclaimed Minister Henry Martin. "Our Groffdale brethren, who are also in the Lancaster Jail had sent a petition to the Supreme Executive Council in Philadelphia. The Council met yesterday and they read our Groffdale brethren's petitions. The Council decided that Peter Summey, Mark Groves, and Christian Martin are free to go home with no fines to pay."[32]

"Completely free, no fine to pay at all!" exclaimed Barbara. "What wonderful Christmas news. I am sure they are having a happy reunion with their families. Are the men who are still in prison writing petitions for mercy also?"

"I will pray that this is the way to go to obtain mercy," replied Bishop Henry Martin. "To help this process along I am going to get signatures attesting to the sincerity and truthfulness of our Weaverland brethren's petitions to the Supreme Executive Council. I am personally planning to deliver Henry Martin's, Christian Carpenter's and Christian Weaver's petitions. I also want to take the Ephrata Cloister's Peter Miller's petition along to the Supreme Executive Council in Philadelphia."

"May I suggest the names of people who I feel would sign, and be recognized as important by the Supreme Executive Council?" faltered the elderly Hans Heinrich. "We can get a whole list of petitioners—local people the Council in Philadelphia does not recognize. We need more petitioners like Peter Miller of the Ephrata Cloister. Retired General Henry Hambright of New Holland is a

---

[32] Peter Summey lived on a tract of land just east of and south of Voganville. He was a descendant of Pioneer Minister Hans Peter Summey. Peter Miller of the Ephrata Cloister signed his petition.

Mark Groves (Groff) apparently was a young man as his petition stated he worked as a laborer and he had no property.

Christian Martin is not listed as a Mennonite and was not on the Earl Township Non-Associators list. *Conscience in Crisis*, pp. 251-255.

friend to the Mennonites. People like this would be noteworthy in the Council's eyes."[33, 34]

"Very good idea," replied Bishop Henry Martin. "There are other captains in the Earl Township Militia, who respect the Mennonite non-resistant faith. They also might sign Henry's petitions."[35]

---

[33] When the Continental Congress fled to Lancaster and York for safety, they printed the Continental money in Ephrata under the direction of Peter Miller. J. I. Mombert, D.D., *Authentic History of Lancaster County* (1839), p. 362.

[34] Henry Hambright's military career began on June 1, 1776, when he enlisted in Earl Township's Militia. He served as a Captain throughout the Revolutionary War. After the war he served as Justice of the Peace in Earl Township. From 1813 to 1817 he was elected to the Pennsylvania State Legislature. In his later years he resided in New Holland. He is buried in the old Welsh Cemetery located on the Eldon Eby Farm between Hinkletown and Terre Hill, Lancaster County, Pa. *Hambrights of Lancaster County / Thomas and Catherine Gorton.*

[35] Four of Henry Martin's petitioners included the title of Captain. Captain Alex M'ilwain: Captain of the First Company of the Fifth Battalion of Lancaster County. This Militia Company of 86 men was where Henry Martin and Henry (Hans) Rutt were supposed to muster to, usually twice a year. Both paid fines instead. Also signing Henry Martin's petition were late Captain John Reeves, Captain Samuel Elaiott, and Captain Henry Hambright. *Pennsylvania Archives, Roll 38 Frame 175.*

CHAPTER 14

February 1, 1783

Elizabeth Furnace

66 I WILL GIVE YOU, our new daughter, the name Judith in remembrance of the grief of mind I am going through with Henry in Lancaster imprisoned in that awful jail," crooned Barbara lovingly, to the newborn baby girl. "I feel my grief is as great as Isaac and Rebekah's, although for a different reason."

Anna, with her curiosity aroused went to Henry and Barbara's big family Bible. "The verses are in Genesis: Chapter 26, Verse 34 and 35," continued Barbara. "Read the verses to me."

Anna opened the Bible and found the verses and read, *"And Esau was forty years old when he took to wife Judith the daughter of Beeri the Hittite, and Bashemath the daughter of Elon the Hittit. Which were a grief of mind unto Isaac and to Rebekah."*

A few days later Minister Henry Martin and his wife came for a visit. After they adored the new baby Judith and shared community news, Bishop Henry announced, "They released another person from prison. On January 30, 1783, the Supreme Executive Council met, and they read Jacob Snyder's petition. Jacob Snyder and his family live near Lancaster. The Council decided to reduce his fine by 66%, which allowed him to pay the rest and go free."

"That is good news," observed Barbara. "I was hoping the rest of the men's fines would be forgiven, like those pardoned on the day before Christmas. Nevertheless, the important thing is, they are freed. How is your plan coming along to gather petitions and travel to Philadelphia?"

"The next Supreme Executive Council meets on February 20, 1783. I have many signatures for Henry's petition. Four Captains of the Continental Army signed the petitions. When I visited with

Peter Miller, he also gave me his personal[36] petition to present to the Council." Pulling a piece of paper from his pocket Minister Henry asked, "Would you like to hear Peter Miller's petition?"

"We would like to hear what the famous Peter Miller has to say about the Mennonite differences with the Continental government," said Barbara.

Minister Henry Martin cleared his throat and read:

Sir,

Having lately been solicited by some Menists who were fined for not apprehending British Deserters, to intercede for them I have ventured to lay their Case before His Excellency, your President. Since that time I have heard that their Fine was considerably lessened, which was an act worthy of your honourable council, and must needs draw upon you the affection of the good people of State. The Bearer hereof, Henry Martin, and another Christian Weaver, who intend at present to address themselves to your honourable board, have also sent down their petition, attested by sundry worthy freeholders; but have hitherto miscarried in their humble expectation. As they are equally entangled with the others in the guilt, it is not probable that their petition should have been rejected, at the same time the council hath extended its mercy over the others.

---

[36] Peter Miller wrote and signed his personal petition. The other petitions were written in English by someone versed in the English language under the direction of the imprisoned Mennonites. The petition was then signed in German Script by the imprisoned Mennonite. Then other men added their own signatures attesting to its truth and sincerity. Peter Milled added his signature to Peter Summey's petition. But for Henry Martin and Christian Weaver, Peter Miller wrote his own personal petition for a plea for mercy.

And therefore, at their desire, I took the freedom to recommend their case, by means of your person, to his excellency and the council. If you think it proper to lay this letter before the president, I desire you to mention my humble respects to Him and family.

I humbly am of opinion that all rulers of governments should be invested with power, to migate the Rigour of the Law by the Interposition of Mercy, when necessary: at least we find thereof many remarkable instances in the Jewish Dispensation. And if this people must pay so great a fine, it is certain they will be ruined, And that for no other crime but neglect of duty in matters they were not permitted to do by their Principles and Conscience. You had been allways considered as an accomplished Politician; and therfore I propose to you the most perfect pattern of sound policy, of a Woman, which was employed by Joab to intercede befor King David for Absalom, 2 Sam.,14,11, when she pray'd that the King would not suffer to multiply in the country the revengers of blood, or as we say now, the informers; for therby the evil is more increased, than lessened. I have no more to add, but that, besides my humble respect to you, I am

Sir, your humble servant, Peter Miller
Ephrata the 9ʰ of Feb.,1783
Directed Timithe Matlack,[37] Esquire Philadelphia. [38]

---

[37] Timothy Matlack, an ex-Quaker, was the President of the Supreme Executive Council. He was noted for his handwriting. He hand wrote the original hand-written Declaration of Independence which is displayed in the National Archives in Washington, D.C.

[38] *Conscience in Crisis*, p. 509.

"Thank you, for your time, effort and concern in this matter," said Barbara. "What happens when the Council in Philadelphia makes their decision?"

"I am going prepared to pay the fine if it is reduced," assured Minister Henry. "Whatever is decided by the Council is recorded, and a letter is written on their decision. I plan to take that letter from Philadelphia to Lancaster and present it to the keeper of the jail. If the fines are paid according to the decisions made in Philadelphia, they are free to come home with me."

"May the Lord bless and keep you as you journey to Philadelphia," said Barbara with tears in her eyes. "The family thanks you for your concern and effort."

A GLORIOUS REUNION—LATE FEBRUARY 1783

"Father is coming in the lane!" shouted Johnny excitedly as he came running back from the springhouse. Johnny completely forgot his chore of fetching water in the excitement of having his father coming home. Soon the whole family was gathered around having a wonderful time of rejoicing. After the excitement settled down everyone sat and Henry stated, "It feels so good to be home. When Minister Henry Martin came with the decree from the Supreme Executive Council, I was so relieved. I was so tired of that prison. They cooped us up in a ten foot by ten foot area with many other men. Many other prisoners were vile and profane. There was no heat, no furniture, only a straw-covered floor."

"What about the rest of the men who were in prison for the same reason you were?" asked Hans Heinrich as he eyed Henry's shabby clothes.

"They released Christian Weaver[39] and Christian Zimmerman with me," Henry replied. "Christian Weaver had to pay a third of his fine, just like me. However, the Supreme Executive Council only reduced Christian Zimmerman's fine a third.[40] They required him to pay two-thirds of his fine to be released. The three Myer's brethren, Abraham, Martin, and Jacob are still in jail, waiting for their petitions to be read in Philadelphia."[41]

"I would suggest that your clothes be burned, and you take a good bath. We do not want to spread prison fever and critters to the rest of the family," suggested Hans Heinrich.

---

[39] Christian Weaver's petition reveals when the British were about to capture Philadelphia. Christian's wagon was used (cheerfully, taken with no resistance) to transport public goods from Philadelphia to safety.

[40] Christian Zimmerman is the only man whose fine was not reduced by two-thirds or completely pardoned. There is no record remaining on why his fine was higher than all the rest.

Some clues to this abnormality are that Peter Miller was silent about Christian Zimmerman on his plea for mercy for the Weberthal brethren. Did this silence influence the Supreme Executive Council? Another possibility, which is from the author with no record to authenticate it, stems back to the trial in Lancaster. The court released Barbara Zimmerman, probably because of Baby Christian Jr. (five months old). Did this reflect on his higher payment?

[41] The petitions of the three Myer's men were read on March 18, 1783. The fines of all three men were reduced by two-thirds, and it is presumed they released them soon after that. The Supreme Executive Council met monthly. If they would not receive their verdict on the meeting held on March 18th, they would have had to pay the full fine. If they could not, they would have received thirty-nine lashes at the post on March 25, 1783.

CHAPTER 15

Mid Fall 1783

Old Trinity Church

Trinity Church

HENRY AND HANS were working in the pasture irrigating the grass for the cattle. It was pleasant work, directing water though various canals. "Christian Carpenter is coming down the road with his horse and two-wheeled cart," observed Henry. "I wonder what he wants? It must be important for him to leave his work in the middle of the day."

"The Continental Congress and Britain have signed a peace treaty," remarked Christian Carpenter, as Hans and Henry clamored up the bank to the farmstead. "They signed the treaty on September 3, 1783. Britain recognizes the United States as an independent country with its own government, not connected to Britain."

"Finally we know who is our Caesar," remarked elderly Hans Heinrich Martin, as he joined the group. "If Britain has released control of the Colonies, our pledge with them is also no longer in effect. We now know which government we should honor."

"After our many hard and difficult experiences with the Colonial Continental Congress the scriptures obligate us to do well to them that despise us," observed Henry. "I am willing to do so, now that we have a clear direction to which government we are subject to."

"Yet not everyone is so willing to accept this new government. Among the Mennonites there is talk about moving to Canada, which is still under the British crown," Christian said. "Many non-Christian loyalists are either moving to Canada, or moving back to England. I would hope that as peace-loving Christians we would not become so involved in our earthly home that we could not accept this new government. They have made practicing nonresistance difficult during the war, but at least they have not forbidden us Mennonites to practice what we believe. I have trust in God, now that peace is here, the unrest in the land will settle down and reason and sanity will prevail."

Hans swung his axe with vigorous anticipation. He was clearing land for his own cabin.

Hans and Anna planned their new farmstead to be on the south side of the Conestoga, almost directly across the stream from Henry Martin's farm. Hans and Anna planned to marry and live there this coming spring. Peace and posterity settled over the Weaverland Valley after the Revolutionary War. The Mennonite Church was prospering and its future looked bright in this new nation called the United States of America.

HISTORICAL
DOCUMENTS

Henry Martin's Petition

Petition Endorsements

Supreme Executive Letter

Christian Weaver's Petition

Christian Zimmerman's Petition

COPY OF HENRY MARTIN'S ORIGINAL PETITION

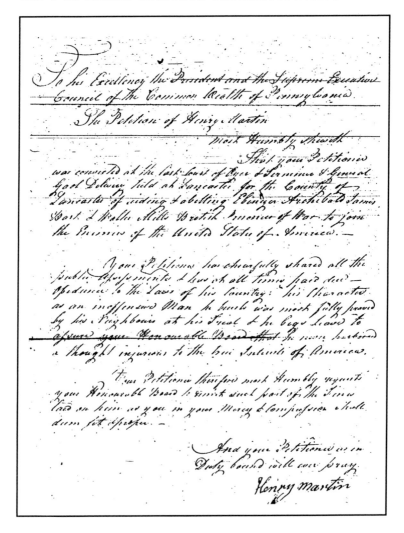

This petition was delivered to the Supreme Executive Council along with the petition of Peter Miller of the Ephrata Cloister. Read to the Supreme Executive Council in Philadelphia on February 20, 1783. The Supreme Executive Council ordered that 2/3 of the monetary charges be forgiven.

HENRY MARTIN'S ORIGINAL PETITION TRANSLATED FROM WRITTEN TO PRINT

To the Excellency the President & the Supreme Executive Council of the Commonwealth of Pennsylvania

The Petition of Henry Martin

Most Humbly Sheweth

That your Petitioner was convicted at the last Court of Oyer & Terminor & General Goal Delivery held at Lancaster in the County of Lancaster of aiding and abetting Ebenezer Archibald & James Bart & Walter Mills British Prisoners of War to join the enemies of the United States of America.

Your Petitioner has cheerfully shared all the public assesstments. I have at all times paid due obedience to the laws of his country His character as an inoffensive man, he trusts was most fully proven by his neighbors at the trial and he begs leave to assure your honorable board that he never harbored a thought injurious to the best interest of America.

Your Petitioner therefore most Humbly requests your Honorable Board to remit such part of the fines laid on him as you in your mercy & compassion deem fit & proper.

And your Petitioner as in Daly
Bound will every pray
Henry Martin

COPY OF HENRY MARTIN'S ORIGINAL PETITION
ENDORSEMENTS

The heading reads: We the Subscribers Humbly beg Leave to recommend the within Petitioners to his Excellency the President of the Supreme Executive Council of the Commonwealth of Pennsylvania for their compassionate attention.

SUPREME EXECUTIVE COUNCIL'S DETERMINATION

The Supreme Executive Council reads petitions, endorsements, and Peter Miller's petition on February 20, 1783. Results are written by Secretary of the Supreme Executive Council. This determination was delivered to Lancaster Sheriff Thomas Edwards.

SUPREME EXECUTIVE COUNCIL'S DETERMINATION
TRANSLATED FROM WRITTEN TO PRINT

In Council   Philadelphia   February 20th 1783

The Petition of Henry Martin convicted of a misdemeanor upon three indictments in the county of Lancaster, for aiding British Prisoners to escape was read. The record of his conviction and a recommendation in his behalf were also read, and the council considered his case.

Ordered that two thirds of the fines be adjudged to be paid to the use of the state by the said Henry Martin be remitted.

The Petition of Christian Weaver convicted of the like offence in the said county praying remission of his fines was read, together with the record of his conviction and a recommendation in his behalf,

On consideration ordered that two thirds of the fines be adjudged to be paid to the use of the state by the said Christian Weaver be remitted.

The Petition of Christian Carpenter convicted of the like offences in the said county praying remission of his fines was read, together with the record of his conviction and a recommendation in his behalf,

On consideration ordered that one third of the fines be adjudged to be paid to the use of the state by the said Christian Carpenter be remitted.

Extract from the Minutes
T Matlack Esq

Thomas Edwards Esq.
Sheriff of Lancaster County

COPY OF CHRISTIAN WEAVER'S ORIGINAL PETITION

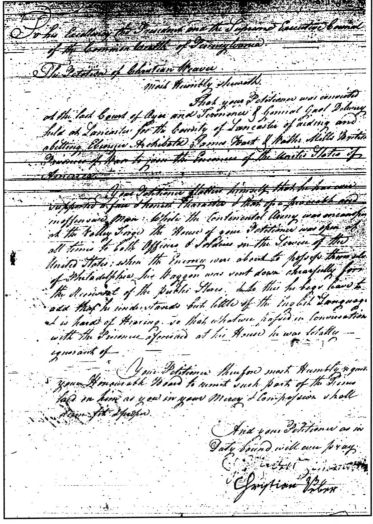

This petition was delivered to the Supreme Executive Council along with the petition of Peter Miller of the Ephrata Cloister. Read to the Supreme Executive Council in Philadelphia on February 20, 1783. The Supreme Executive Council ordered that 2/3 of the monetary charges be forgiven.

CHRISTIAN WEAVER'S ORIGINAL PETITION TRANSLATED FROM WRITTEN TO PRINT

To his Excellency, The President and the Supreme Executive Council of the Commonwealth of Pennsylvania

The Petition of Christian Weaver

Most Humbly Sheweth

That your Petitioner was convicted at the last Court of Oyer and Terminer and General Goal Delivery held at Lancaster for the County of Lancaster the sixteenth day of October 1782, for aiding and abetting Ebenezer Archibald, James Bard, and Walter Mills British Prisoners of War to join the enemies of the United States of America.

Your petitioner flatters himself that he has ever supported a fair and honest character and that he is a peaceable and inoffensive man. While the Continental army was encamping at the Valley Forge the house of your petitioner was open at all times to both officers and Soldiers in the Service of the United States: When the enemy was about to possess themselves of Philadelphia his wagon was sent down chearfully for the removal of Public stores. To this he begs leave to add that he understands but little of the English language and is hard of hearing, so that whatever passed in conversation with the prisoners aforesaid at his house he was totally ignorant of.

Your Petitioner therefore most humbly requests your Honourable Board to remit such part of the fines laid on him as you in your mercy shall deem fit and proper.

And your Petitioner as in
Duty bound will ever pray.
Christian Weaver

COPY OF CHRISTIAN ZIMMERMAN'S ORIGINAL PETITION

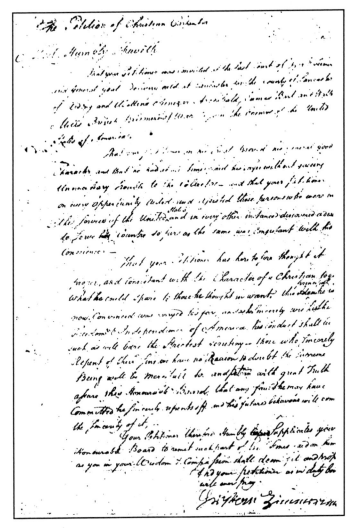

Read to the Supreme Executive Council in Philadelphia on February 20, 1783. The Supreme Executive Council orderd that 1/3 of the monetary charges be forgiven. Christian Carpenter/Zimmerman was the only one who had only 1/3 of the fines forgiven. All the rest of those charged with him had all of or 2/3 of the fines forgiven.

CHRISTIAN ZIMMERMAN'S ORIGINAL PETITION
TRANSLATED FROM WRITTEN TO PRINT

The Petition of Christian Carpenter (signed Christian Zimmerman)

Most Humbly Showeth
      That your petitioner was convicted at the last court of Oyer wherein General Goal delivery held at Lancaster in the county of Lancaster of aiding and abetting Ebenezer Archiblad, James Bart, and Walter Mills British prisoner of war to join the enemies of the United States of America.
      That your petitioner on ???? proved his general good character, and that he had at all times paid his payor without ???? ???? trouble to the collector—and that your petitioner on every opportunity aided and assisted these persons who were in the services of the United States and in every other instance discovered a desire to serve his country, so far as the same was constant with his conscience.
      What your petitioner has here to fore thought it proper and consistent with the character of a Christian to give what he could spare to those he thought in want. This idea he is now Convinced was carried too far and sincerely wishist Freedom and Independence of America. His conduct shall be such as will bare the strictest scrutiny. Those who sincerely repent of their sins have no reason to doubt the Supreme being will be merciful to. and petition with great truth afar this honorable board, that any fault he may have committed, he sincerely repents off, and his future behavior will commence the sincerity of it.
      Your Petitioner therefore Humbly supplicates your honorable Board to remit such part of his fines laid on him, as you in your wisdom and Compassion shall deem fit and proper.

> And your petitioner as is duty bound
> Wile mor pray
> Christian Zimmerman

Epilogue

THE CONTINENTAL CONGRESS gave way to the Constitution of the United States. The Constitution was drawn up by 55 delegates to the Constitutional Convention in Philadelphia during the summer of 1787 and ratified by the States in 1788. This system of government we know today as the United States of America. A government Christians are obligated to pray for and be thankful for. The Continental Congress government was intolerant of nonconformity and nonresistance, but the seed it planted has grown into a land of many privileges. Freedom, complete freedom to practice nonresistance and nonconformity. We have complete freedom to worship our redeemer, the Lord Jesus Christ as taught in the Bible, with no hindrances or fear from the government authorities. But the trials and sufferings of our ancestors earned this freedom. This account is just one of many struggles the Mennonites, the Amish, the Quakers, and other peace churches endured. By their faithfulness, the new government grudgingly granted American citizens the religious freedom we have today. May we be thankful for the price they paid for us.

The elderly Hans Heinrich Martin passed on to his eternal reward in October of 1784. He was buried in Zimmerman Cemetery, near Lichty's Church.

Revolutionary Adventure

PRINTED IN THE *NEW ENGLAND MAGAZINE*[42]
September 1831

The leading events of the War of Independence are familiar to every American; but many incidents, full of interest and adventure, yet remain to be disclosed. There are those yet living who remember the following story.

The American authorities found much difficulty in disposing of their prisoners. They had no posts regularly fitted for the purpose; and they could suggest no better means for securing them, then to place them under guard in a thickly settled part of the country, where the inhabitants were most decidedly hostile to the English. The town of Lancaster, in Pennsylvania, was of those selected for this purpose. The prisoners were confined in barracks, enclosed with a stockade and vigilantly guarded. But in spite of all the precautions, they often disappeared in an unaccountable manner, and nothing was heard of them till they resumed their place in the British army. Many and various were the conjectures as to the means of their escape; the officers inquired and investigated

---

[42] The author did some minor editing to make it suitable for younger readers.

in vain; the county was explored to no purpose; the soldiers shook their heads, and told of fortune-tellers, peddlers and such characters, who had been seen at intervals; and sundry of the more credulous could think of nothing but the supernatural agency; but whether man or spirit was the conspirator, the mystery was unbroken.

When this became known to Washington, he sent General Hazen to take this responsible charge. This energetic officer, after exhausting all resources, resorted to stratagem. He was convinced that, as the nearest post was more than a hundred miles distant, the prisoners must be aided by Americans, but where the suspicion should fall he could not even conjecture; the reproach of Toryism being almost unknown in that region. Having been trained to meet exigencies of this kind in a distinguished career, as a colonel in the British army, his plan was formed at once, and communicated to an officer of his own, upon whose talent he relied for its successful execution. This was Captain Lee, whose courage and ability fully justified the selection.

The secret plan concerted between them was this. It was to be given out that Lee was absent on furlough or command. He in the meantime was to assume the dress of a British prisoner, and having provided himself with information and a story of his capture, was to be thrown into the barracks, where he might gain the confidence of the soldiers, and join them in a plan of escape.

How well Captain Lee sustained his part may be inferred from the fact that when he had disappeared and placed himself among the prisoners, his own officers and soldiers saw him every day without the least suspicion. The person to whom I am indebted for most of these particulars was the Intendant of the prisoners, and familiar with Lee; but, being compelled to see him often in the discharge of his duty, he never penetrated the disguise. Well it was for Lee that his disguise was so complete. Had his associates suspected his purpose to betray them, his history would have been embraced in the proverb, "dead men tell no tales."

For many days he remained in this situation, making no discoveries whatever. He thought he perceived at times of intelligence between the prisoners and an old woman, who was allowed to bring fruit for sale within the enclosure. She was known to be deaf and half-witted, and was therefore no object of suspicion. It was known that her son had been disgraced and punished in the American army, but she never betrayed any malice on that account, and no one dreamed that she could have any power to do injury if she processed the will. Lee watched her closely, but saw nothing to confirm his suspicions. Her dwelling was about a mile distant, in a wild retreat, where she shared her miserable quarters with a dog and cat, the former of which mounted a guard over her mansion, while the latter encouraged superstitious fears which were equally effectual in keeping visitors away.

One dark stormy night in autumn, he was lying awake at midnight, meditating on the enterprise he had undertaken, which, though in the beginning it had recommended itself to his romantic disposition, and now lost all its charms. It was one of those tempests, which in our climate so often hang upon the path of the departing year.

His companions slept soundly, but the wind which shook the building to its foundation and shew heavy splashes of rain against the windows, conspired with the state of his mind to keep him wakeful. All at once the door was gently opened, and a figure moved silently into the room. It was too dark to observe its motions narrowly, but he could see that it stooped towards one of the sleepers who immediately rose; next it approached him and touched him on the shoulder. Lee immediately started up; the figure then allowed a slight gleam from the dark lantern to pass over his face, and as it did so whispered impatiently, "Not the man—but come!" It then occurred to Lee that this was the moment he desired. The unknown whispered to him to keep his place till another man was called; but just at that moment some noise disturbed him, and making a sign to Lee to follow, he moved silently out of the room.

They found the door of the house unbarred, and a small part of the fence removed, where they passed out without molestation; the sentry had retired to a shelter where he thought he could guard his post without suffering from the rain; but Lee saw that his conductors put themselves in preparation to silence him if he should happen to address them. Just without the fence appeared a stooping figure, wrapped in a red cloak and supporting itself with a large stick, which Lee at once perceived could be none other than the old fruit woman. But the most profound silence was observed; a man came out from a thicket at a little distance and joined them, and the whole party moved onward under the guidance of the old woman. At first they frequently stopped to listen, but having heard the sentinel's cry "all's well," they seemed reassured and moved with more confidence than before.

They soon came near to her cottage under an overhanging bank, where a bright light was shining out from a little window upon the wet and drooping boughs that hung near it. The dog received them graciously, and they entered. A table was set with some course provisions upon it, which one of the soldiers was about to seize, when the man who conducted them withheld him. "No," said he, "we must first proceed to business." He then went to a small closet, from which he returned with what seemed to have been originally a Bible, though now it was worn to a mahogany color and a spherical form.

While they were doing this, Lee had time to examine his companions; one of whom was a large quiet looking soldier, the other a short stout man with much the aspect of a villain. They examined him in turn. And as Lee had been obliged formerly to punish the shorter soldier severely, he felt some misgivings when the fellow's eyes rested upon him. Their conductor was a middle-aged harsh-looking man, whom Lee had never seen before.

As no time was to be lost, their guide explained to them in few words, that, before he would undertake his dangerous enterprise, he should require of them to swear upon the scriptures, not to make the least attempt to escape, and never to reveal the circumstances or agents in the proceedings, whatever might befall them. The soldiers however, insisted on deferring this measure till they had formed a slight acquaintance with contents on the table, and expressed their sentiments on the subject rather by actions than words. In this they were joined by Lee, who by this time had begun to contemplate the danger of his enterprise in a new and unpleasant view. If he were to be compelled to accompany his party to New York, his disguise would at once be detected, and it was certain that he would be hanged as a spy. He supposed beforehand, that he should find no difficulty in escaping at any moment: but he saw that their conductor had prepared arms for them, which they were to use in taking the life of anyone who should attempt to leave them, and then the oath. He might possibly have released himself from its obligations, when it came necessary for the interests of his country; but no honorable man can well bear to be driven to an emergency; in which he must violate an oath, however reluctantly it was taken. He felt there was no retreating, when there came a heavy shock, as of something falling against the sides of the house; their practiced ears at once detected the alarm gun; their conductor throwing down the old Bible, which he had held all the while impatiently in his hand, directed the party to follow him in close order, and immeaditly quitted the house. Taking with him the dark lantern.

They went on with great dispatch, but not without difficulty. Sometimes their footing would give away on some sandy bank or slippery field; and when their path led through the woods, the wet boughs dashed heavily in their faces. Lee felt that he might have deserted his precious companions while they were in this hurry and alarm; but he felt, that, as yet he had made no discoveries; and however dangerous his situation was, he could not bear to confess that he has not the nerve to carry it through. On he went, therefore, for two or three hours, and was beginning to sink with fatigue, when the barking of a dog brought the party to a stand. Their conductor gave a low whistle, which was answered at no great distance, and a figure came forward in the darkness, who whispered to their guide, and then led the way up to a building, which seemed by the shadowy outline, to be a large stone barn.

They entered it, and were severally placed in small nooks where they could feel there was hay all around them, except on the side of the wall. Shortly after, some provisions were brought to them with the same silence, and it was signified to them that they were to remain concealed through the whole of the coming day.

Through a crevice in the wall Lee could discover, as the day came on, that the barn was attached to a small farmhouse. He was so near to the house that he could overhear the conversations which were carried on about the door. The morning rose clear, and it was evident from the horsemen, which occasionally galloped up to the door, that the country was alarmed. The farrmer gave short and surly replies, as if unwilling to be taken off from his labor; but the other inmates of the house were eager in their questions, and, from the answers

Lee gathered that the means by which he and his companions had escaped were as mysterious as ever.

The next night, when all was quiet, they resumed their march, and explained to Lee that, as he was not with them in their conspiracy and was accidentally associated with them in their escape, they should take the precaution to keep him before them, just behind the guide. He submitted without opposition, though the arrangement considerably lessened the changes in favor of his escape. He observed, from the direction of the stars, that they did not move in a direct line toward the Delaware, but changed the course so often that he could not conjecture at what point they intended to strike the river. He endeavored, whenever any peculiar object appeared, to fix it in his memory as well as the darkness would permit, and succeeded better than could have been expected, considering the agitated state in which he traveled.

For several nights they went on in this manner, being delivered over to different persons, from time to time; as Lee could gather from the whispered conversations, they were regularly employed on occasions like the present, and well rewarded by the British for their services. Their employment was full of danger: and though they seemed like desperate men, he could observe that they never remitted their precautions. They were concealed by day in barns-cellars-caves made for the purpose, and similar retreats, and one day passed in a tomb, the dimensions which had been enlarged, and the inmates, if there had been any, banished to make room for the living. The burying grounds were a favorite retreat, and on more occasions than one they were obliged to resort to superstitious alarms to remove intruders upon their path; their success fully justified the experiment, and, unpleasantly situated as he was, in prospect of soon being a ghost himself, he could not avoid laughing at the expedition with which old and young fled from the fancied apparitions under the clouds of night, wishing to meet such enemies like Ajax, in the face of day.

Though the distance to the Delaware was not great, they had now been twelve days on the road, and such was the vigilance and suspicion prevailing throughout the country, that they almost despaired of effecting their object. The conductor grew impatient, and Lee's companions, at least one of them, became ferocious. There was, as we have said, something unpleasant to him in the glances of this fellow toward him, which became more and more fierce as they went on: but it did appear whether it was owing to circumstances or actual suspicion. It so happened that on the twelfth night, Lee was placed in a barn, while the rest of the party sheltered themselves in the cellar of a little stone church, where they could talk and act with more freedom, both because of the solitude of the church was not often disturbed, even on the Sabbath, because the proprietors did not know that illegal hands had added a cellar to the conveniences of the building.

The party was seated there as the day broke, and the light which struggled in through the crevices opened for the purpose, showed a low room about twelve feet square, with a damp floor and large patches of white mold upon the walls. Finding probably, that the pavement offered no accommodation for sleeping, the worthies were seated each upon a little cask, which seemed like those used for gunpowder. The short soldier asked in a careless way if they knew who they had in their party. The other startled and asked him what he meant. "I mean," said he, "that we are honored with the company of Captain Lee, of the rebel army. The rascal once punished me, and I never mistook a man when I have debt of that kind to pay. Now I will have my revenge."

The others hastened to express their disgust at his ferocity, saying that if, as he said, their companion was an American officer, all they had to do was to watch him closely. They said that, as he had come among them uninvited, he must go with them to New York and take the consequences: but meantime it was their interest, not to seem to suspect him, otherwise he might give an alarm, whereas it was evidently his intentions to go with them till they were ready to embark for New York. The other persisted in saying he would have his revenge with his own hand, upon which the conductor, drawing a pistol declared to him that if he saw the least attempt to injure Captain Lee, or any conduct which would lead him to suspect that his disguise was discovered, he would at that moment shoot him through the head. The soldier put his hand upon his knife with an ominous scowl upon his conductor, but seeing he had to do with one who was likely to be as good as his word, he restrained himself, and began to arrange some rubbish to serve him for a bed. The other soldier followed his example, and their guide withdrew, locking the door after him.

The next night they went on as usual, but the manner of their conductor showed that there was more danger than before; in fact he explained to the party, that they were not far from the Delaware, and hoped to reach it before midnight. They occasionally heard the report of a musket, which seemed to indicate that some movement was going on in the country. Thus warned, they quickened their steps, and it was not long before they saw a gleam of broad clear light before them, such as is reflected from calm water even in the darkest night. They moved up to it with deep silence; there were various emotions in their breasts; Lee was hoping for an opportunity to escape from an enterprise which was growing too serious, and the principal objects of which were already answered: the others were anxious lest some accident might have happened to the boat on which they depended for crossing the stream.

When they came to the bank there were no traces of a boat on the waters. Their conductor stood still for a moment in dismay; but collecting himself, he said it was possible it might have been secured lower down the stream, and forgetting everything else, he directed the larger soldier to accompany him, and giving a pistol to the other, he whispered, "If the rebel officer attempts to betray us shoot him, shoot him; if not, you will not, for your own sake, make any noise to show where we are." In the same instant they departed and Lee was left alone with the ruffian.

He had before suspected that the fellow knew him, and now doubts were changed to certainty at once. Dark as it was, it seemed as if fire flashed from his eye, now he felt revenge was in his power. Lee was as brave as any officer in the army; but he was unarmed, and though he was strong, his adversary was still more powerful. While he stood, uncertain what to do, the fellow seemed enjoying the prospect of revenge, as he looked upon him with a steady eye. Though the officer stood to appearance unmoved, the sweat rolled in heavy drops from his brow. He soon took his resolution, and sprang upon his adversary, with the intention of wresting the pistol from his hand; but the other was upon his guard, and aimed with such precision, that had the pistol been charged with a bullet, that moment would have been his last. But it seems the conductor had trusted to the sight of his weapons to render the use of them unnecessary, and had therefore loaded them only with powder; as it was, the shock threw Lee to the ground; but fortunately, as the fellow dropped the pistol, it fell to where Lee could reach it, as his adversary stooped, and was drawing a knife from his bosom, Lee was able to give him a stunning blow. He immediately thew himself upon the assassin, and a long struggle began; they were nearly matched in strength and advantage, that neither dared to unclench their hold for the sake of grasping the knife. The combat would probably have in favor of the assassin, when steps and voices were heard advancing, and they found themselves in the hands of countrymen, who were armed for the occasion, and were scouring the banks of the river. They were forcibly torn apart, but so exhausted and breathless, that neither could make any explanations, and they submitted quietly to the disposal of their captors.

The party of armed countrymen, thought they had succeeded in their attempt, and were sufficiently triumphant on the occasion, were sorely perplexed to determine how to dispose of their prisoners. After some discussion, one of them proposed to throw the decision upon the wisdom of the nearest magistrate. They accordingly proceeded to his mansion, about two miles distant, and called on him to rise and attend to business. A window was hastily thrown up, and the justice put forth his night-capped head, and, with more wrath than became his dignity, ordered them off; and in requital for their calling him out of bed in the cold, generously wished them to depart. However, resistance was vain; he was compelled to rise; and as soon as the prisoners were brought before him, he ordered them to be taken in irons to the prison in Philadelphia. Lee improved the opportunity to take the old gentleman aside; and told him who he was, and why he was disguised; the justice only interrupted him with an occasional inquiry, "Most done:" When he was finished, the magistrate told him that his story was well made, and told in a manner very creditable to his address, and that he should give it all the weight which it seemed to require. All Lee's remonstrations were unavailing.

As soon as they were fairly lodged in prison, Lee prevailed on the jailer to carry a note to General Lincoln, informing him of his condition. The General received it as he was dressing in the morning, and immediately sent one of his aids to the jail. That officer could not believe his eyes when he saw Captain Lee. His uniform, worn when he had assumed it, was now hanging in rags about him, and he had not been shaved for a fortnight; he wished, very naturally, to improve his appearance before presenting himself before the Secretary of War; but the orders were peremptory to bring him as he was. The General loved a joke full well; his laughter was hardly exceeded by the report of his own cannon; and long and loud did he laugh that day.

When General Lee returned to Lancaster, he immediately attempted to retrace the ground; and so accurate, under all the unfavorable circumstances, had been his investigation, that he brought to justice fifteen persons, who had aided the escape of British prisoners. It is hardly necessary to say to those who know the fate of revolutionary officers, that he received, for this hazardous and effectual service, no reward whatever.

THOMAS MCKEAN

The presiding judge at the Mennonites' trial in Lancaster. He was an avid supporter of the Revolution and had a sharp temper. He always carried a cane with a gold head.

TIMOTHY MATLACK

He was famous for his beautiful handwriting. The handwritten original Declaration of Independence archived in Washington, D.C., was written by him. Timothy Matlack was secretary of the Supreme Executive Council during the reading of the Mennonites' petitions.

A Review

Information and supporting documentation gleaned about Lancaster Men and Women, who were not expounded on in *Mennonites in Crisis*. They were also charged on October 15 to 20, 1782, for seditiously and treacherously assisting the enemy. These men and women, would merit further study as *Mennonites in Crisis* focuses on the Weaverland Brethren.

PETER SUMMEY, a Mennonite from the Groffdale area living just outside of Voganville. He was a nephew of the Pioneer Mennonite preacher at Groffdale by the same name. His petition states he has six children, with the three eldest being deaf and dumb. His petition mentioning six children positively identifies him. Petition read on December 24, 1782 (Christmas Eve) and all fines remitted.

Author has a copy of Peter Summey's original petition to the Supreme Executive Council.

Also, a copy of Petitioners for Peter Summey including the signature of Peter Miller.

MARK GROVES, a Mennonite from the Groffdale area. His petition states he owned no property and was a daily laborer

Petition read on December 24,1782 (Christmas Eve) and all fines remitted..

Author has a copy of Mark Groves original petition to the Supreme Executive Council.

CHRISTIAN MARTIN, is not listed as a Mennonite on the Earl Township's non -associaters list of 1775, but was processed with others from Groffdale so it is presumed he was also from the Groffdale area

Petition read on December 24,1782 (Christmas Eve) and all fines remitted.

Author has a copy of Christian Martin's original petition to the Supreme Executive Council.

NOTE: Concerning the three following Myers men—On August 22, 1780, in the Township of Manheim, a Charles Hall appraised horses, Fore geers, and bags apparently taken from Abram, Martin, and Jacob Myers by the United States of America for wagon service. If the Myers were from Manheim Township they would not have been on Earl Township's non -associaters list of 1775, so there is a possibility they were also Mennonites, *Conscience in Crisis* Page *347*.

ABRAHAM MYERS, is not listed on the Earl Township non -associaters list of 1775. His petition states that he a young Man with an infirmity of the body   His petition was read on December 22, 1782 Ordered that two thirds of the fine be remitted .

Author has a copy of Abraham Myers's original petition to the Supreme Executive Council.

MARTIN MYERS, is not listed on the Earl Township's non -associaters list of 1775. All of the men where to receive 39 lashes at the whipping post if fine was not paid till March 5th. But Martin Myers was excused from this stipulation. His petition was read on December 22, 1782, and it was ordered half of his fine remitted.

Author has a copy of Martin Myers's original petition to the Supreme Executive Council.

JACOB MYERS, is not listed on the Earl Township's non -associaters list of 1775. Jacob Myers was told to exit the first trial immeaditly, with Barbra Carpenter and Ann Shirk. At the trial on October 20th, Jacob was pronounced guilty. His petition reveals he lived within two miles of Lancaster. His petition was read on December 22, 1782 and it was ordered a complete remission of fines.

Author has a copy of Jacob Myers's original petition to the Supreme Executive Council.

JACOB SNYDER, Not listed on the Earl Township non -associaters list of 1775 , but possibly lived outside of Earl Township

Petition read January 30, 1783. His petition reveals he had a British Prisoner of War (Very Common) working for him named Richard Lillus. Escaped prisoners of war came to see Richard Lillus.

Jacob Snyder has a small 100 acre farm, which was not paid for.

He also had six children with one child having a broken leg. Ordered two -thirds of fine be remitted.

Author has a copy of Jacob Snyder's original petition to the Supreme Executive Council.

CHRISTIAN GROVES, not identified as a Mennonite, but is on the Earl Township's non -associaters list of 1775.

Was fined 150 pounds at court trial while most were fined 50 pounds His petition was read on December 2, 1782.

Ordered two -thirds of fine be remitted

Author has a copy of the original order from Supreme Executive Council to the sheriff of Lancaster of Lancaster County concerning Christian Groves.

JACOB GROVES, not identified as a Mennonite, but is on the Earl Township's non -associaters list of 1775.

Was fined 150 pounds at court trial while most were fined 50 pounds. Petition reveals he is an aged and infirm man and cannot understand or speak any English. His petition was read on December 1, 1782.

Ordered two -thirds of fine be remitted

Author has a copy of the original order from Supreme Executive Council to the sheriff of Lancaster of Lancaster County concerning Jacob Groves.

ANN SHIRK, no supporting documents. Ordered to exit on October 15th trial, and found not guilty on a trial held on October 20th 1782. Was She the fruit women?

MARK MARTIN, not listed on the Earl Township's non -associaters list of 1775.

He was Sick on day of trial and not present.

PETER GROVES, not listed on the Earl Township's non -associaters list of 1775, and was found not guilty.

JOSEPH RUPP, a Mennonite on the Earl Township's non -associaters list of 1775, and was found not guilty.